WORKBOOK FOR PERSPECTIVES IN MUSIC THEORY

VOLUME I

WORKBOOK FOR PERSPECTIVES IN MUSIC THEORY

SECOND EDITION

PAUL COOPER

Shepherd School of Music
Rice University

1817

HARPER & ROW, PUBLISHERS, New York
Cambridge, Hagerstown, Philadelphia, San Francisco,
London, Mexico City, São Paulo, Sydney

WORKBOOK FOR PERSPECTIVES IN MUSIC THEORY, SECOND EDITION, VOLUME I

Copyright © 1981 by Harper & Row

ISBN: 0-06-041374-3

223990

CONTENTS

CONTENTS

PREFACE

The workbooks that accompanied the first edition of *Perspectives in Music Theory* were written at the request of many colleagues throughout the United States and Canada who desired complementary materials for the basic text. Comments from both students and teachers strongly suggest that the workbooks do help in the teaching and learning of music theory and in the development of a solid musicianship. I very much hope that the present revised volume will be of even greater value.

Volume I is correlated with Chapters 1 through 15 of the text. The objectives of this volume are specific and include the following

1. To support and complement the theoretical concepts presented in the text
2. To assist the student in acquiring fluency in music fundamentals and basic writing skills
3. To provide additional analytical examples for the student's investigation
4. To develop compositional skills for each student as appropriate to individual professional needs and personal interests
5. To introduce the student to the basic pedagogy of theory

Five different kinds of individual assignments are included in the *Workbook*: Studies, Programs, Reviews, Fundamentals Quizzes, and Final Projects. These assignments are correlated with the concepts presented in the text. Many of the Studies require the student to identify, define, and analyze musical terminology, concepts, and passages of actual music literature, and also to compose short works in the style of compositions studied. Final Projects include suggestions for longer papers and for in-depth analyses of music.

Variety is an important aspect of the teaching and learning process. To approach a theoretical concept or piece of music from several different standpoints is pedagogically sound as well as of vital importance in stimulating the student to examine the totality of musical sound.

The workbooks have an efficient and time-saving format. The teacher is invited to omit certain Studies and to substitute others that are particularly instructive. Although the text and the workbooks provide an abundance of Suggested Studies, it should be kept in mind that the ultimate goal is not quantity but *quality*. To work unswervingly for pefection is to imitate the art of music itself.

Paul Cooper

WORKBOOK FOR PERSPECTIVES IN MUSIC THEORY

Chapter 1
MUSICAL THEORY
Musical Aesthetics

STUDIES

1. The ability to speak and write lucidly about the art and science of sound is of great importance to the developing musician. In order to attain these skills it is not only necessary to have a command of the language, but to have comprehension and command of the vocabulary and concepts related to the field of music as well. An excellent place to begin to acquire such comprehension is with the standard music dictionaries in the English language.

    Grove's Dictionary of Music and Musicians (5th ed.) defines the word *aesthetics* as "the theory of artistic experience." The *Harvard Dictionary of Music* (Willi Apel) defines *musical aesthetics* as "the study of the relationship of music to the human senses and intellect."

    Find at least two definitions of the word *music*, including the one in the *Harvard Dictionary of Music*. Note your sources.

    Music:

    Music:

2. Be able to discuss in class, or write a one-page paper on, one of the following topics. If writing a paper, note the list of research materials provided after the topics, which will aid you in the formal construction of your paper.

    Music as a utilitarian function

    Music as entertainment

    The relationship of folk music to art music

    Music as an extension of reality

    Demar Irvine. *Writing About Music: A Style Book for Reports and Theses.* Seattle: University of Washington Press, 1956.

    The MLA Style Sheet. 2nd ed. New York: Modern Language Association of America, 1970.

    Kate L. Turabian. *A Manual for Writers of Term Papers, Theses, and Dissertations.* 3rd ed. Chicago: University of Chicago Press, 1967.

1

3. Music is classified as either a *heteronomous* art or an *autonomous* art. Probably the truth lies somewhere in between. However, one illustration of these two aesthetic concepts can be found in the conflicting ideals of *program music* and *absolute music.*

a. Find definitions of both terms.

Program music:

Absolute music:

b. Listen to two symphonic works (if possible, while following the musical scores).

Mozart — Symphony in G Minor, K. 550

Richard Strauss — *Ein Heldenleben*

c. Discuss the two works briefly below in light of the concepts of program music and absolute music.

INSTRUCTIONS FOR LEARNING PROGRAMS

1. Cover the left-hand column with a marker.

2. Study the information of each frame and respond to the question(s) or provide the missing word(s).

3. Uncover the left-hand column and compare your answers. Mark all errors. Consult the text, additional sources, or the instructor on any items that remain unclear.

   Note: Students who have had little or no formal training in music theory may wish to study a complete program of theory fundamentals such as either of the following:

   John Clough. *Scales, Intervals, Keys and Triads: A Programed Book of Elementary Music Theory.* New York: W. W. Norton, 1964.

   Paul Harder. *Basic Materials in Music Theory: A Programed Course.* 2nd ed. Boston: Allyn and Bacon, 1970.

PROGRAM I

ACOUSTICAL AND PHYSICAL PROPERTIES OF SOUND

1. SOUND

   1. Music is the art and science of organized sound, in time. In other words, the two main properties of music are time and _____.

2. SOUND

   2. Sound is studied in a science called *acoustics.* Acoustics examines the properties of _____.

3. ELASTIC BODY

   3. Sound is generated by a vibrating elastic body, such as a string or a column of air. Sound is generated by a vibrating _____ _____.

4. ACOUSTICS

   4. Various physical properties of sound will be discussed in this chapter. The science that studies sound is called _____.

5. SOUND

   5. The acoustical properties to be studied are frequency (pitch), amplitude (intensity), and timbre. These are all properties of _____.

6. FREQUENCY

6. The term *frequency* refers to the number of vibrations *per second* of the elastic body. Four hundred and forty vibrations per second refers to the _____ of vibrations of the instrument that is generating sound.

7. FREQUENCY

7. *Pitch* is a subjective term describing highness or lowness of sound. Pitch is determined by the number of vibrations per second, or_____.

8. PITCH

8. The number of vibrations per second of the elastic body is called frequency and determines_____.

9. HIGHNESS, LOWNESS

9. The relative term *pitch* refers to the_____ or_____ of a sound.

10. a

10. The *fewer* vibrations per second, the lower the pitch will be. If two given notes have the frequency of (a) 220 and (b) 440, which will sound lower, a or b?_____

Chapter 2
THE NOTATED PAGE
NOTATION

REVIEW

1. The signs, symbols, and words which comprise musical notation have both a specific _____ and a precise _____.

2. Since the time of _____ (composer or period) most tempi have been indicated.

3. The invention of the staff (four line) is credited to _____ about the year _____.

4. Clefs indicate the location of a specific _____.

5.

   Although all clefs are moveable, it is the C clef in particular that is often so used. Its midpoint always designates middle C. With this in mind, write the names of the following notes:

   ____   ____   ____   ____

6.

   Write the names of the following notes:

   ____   ____   ____   ____

7. A key signature constitutes an _____ of pitches that require either a sharp or a flat.

8. Since about the year _____, time signatures have been employed in notated music to indicate the number and kind of duration units (beats) contained within a measure.

9. Two types of early notation are called _____ and _____.

SUPPLEMENTARY MATERIAL FOR CHAPTER 2

PROGRAM II

1. NO RESPONSE

   1. The grand staff consists of two staves (usually treble and bass clefs) joined by a vertical line and a brace. It is most commonly used for piano music.

   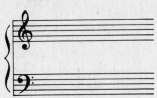

2. LEGER LINES

   2. The range of a staff may be extended by the use of leger lines above or below the staff.

   An extension of the range of a staff is achieved by employing_____.

3. OCTAVE SIGN

   3. To avoid using too many leger lines and to facilitate reading, the octave (It., *ottava*) sign is used (8va - - - - -). When placed above a note or group of notes it means that they are to sound an octave higher.

   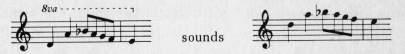

   The indication 8va - - - - - - is called an _____ _____.

   Where would this pitch sound? Write it on the staff provided without using the octave sign.

   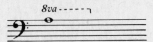 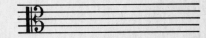

4.

   4. When the octave sign is placed below a note or group of notes, they are to sound an octave lower.

   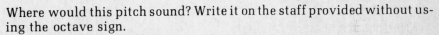

   Where would this pitch sound?

   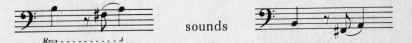

5. NO RESPONSE

   5. The indication 15ma (It., *quindicesima*) is used above or below a group of notes that sound *two octaves* from the original.

6.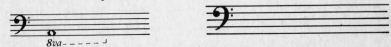

   6. An additional notational practice uses a small 8 below the treble clef. All pitches following this sign will sound one octave lower.

   Where would this pitch sound?

   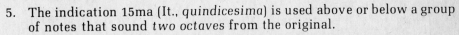

Chapter 3
HARMONIC SERIES, OCTAVE IDENTIFICATION, SCALES, INTERVALS, KEY SIGNATURES

PROGRAM III

1. FREQUENCY

1. A sound whose pitch is "higher" than that of another given sound will have a greater _____ .

2. PITCH

2. *Highness* and *lowness* refer to the _____ of a given sound.

3. 220

3. Frequency and pitch are directly proportional. For example, if the frequency of a pitch is doubled, the resulting sound will be one octave higher. If the frequency is halved, the resulting pitch is one octave lower. If the pitch of a given sound is equal to 440 vibrations per second, the pitch one octave above will have a frequency of 880. One octave below 440, the frequency will be _____ .

4. a. 90
   c. 360
   d. 720

4. Give the frequency of the following notes: a.___ b. 180 c.___ d.___ .

5. NO RESPONSE

5. Amplitude is the amount of energy effecting the vibration of the body. Amplitude determines the intensity of the sound produced.

6. AMPLITUDE

6. The intensity of a sound is determined by its_____.

7. PITCH

7. Intensity is determined by amplitude. Frequency determines _____.

8. TIMBRE

8. An additional physical property of sound is *timbre*, which refers to quality of sound produced. The quality of a sound is known as _____.

9. UPPER PARTIALS

9. Every sound source has a distinctive timbre, which is determined by the fundamental and upper partials of the sound it produces. Depending on the sound sources, these partials vary in number and relative intensity. Sounds are a complex comprised of a fundamental and _____ .

10. UPPER PARTIALS, OVERTONES

10. The partials above the fundamental are known as *overtones*. This set of upper partials, or overtones, is known as the *harmonic* or *overtone series*. The overtone series is composed of a fundamental and _____, _____ or _____.

11. FUNDAMENTAL

11. The harmonic series is a set of partials, composed of overtones above a _____ .

12. OVERTONES, UPPER PARTIALS

12. The harmonic series consists of a fundamental and its _____, or _____.

13. HARMONICS

13. Another term with the same meaning as overtones is *harmonics*. Overtones are the same as_____.

14. YES

14. The beginning of the harmonic series produced by C is shown.

The interval structure of all harmonic series is the same. Will the fourth partial always be two octaves above the fundamental? (yes/no)_____ .

OCTAVE IDENTIFICATION

1. OCTAVE

1. Of all intervals the octave is considered to be the most perfect consonance. Its frequency ratio (of cycles, or vibrations, per second) is 1 : 2 from any given pitch upward. The_____is a natural phenomenon that has been referred to as the "basic miracle of music."

2. e^i

2. The commonly employed octave designations are cited below.

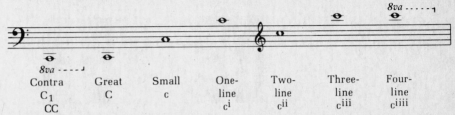

Contra C_1 CC	Great C	Small c	One-line c^i	Two-line c^{ii}	Three-line c^{iii}	Four-line c^{iiii}

All other pitches are reckoned above the C designated for that octave. Thus,

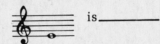 is_____.

3. 880

3. One octave above a^i = 440 is a^{ii} =_____.

4. a = 220

4. One octave below a^i = 440 is_____=_____.

5. OCTAVE

5. The interval that seems to duplicate the pitch of the basic note, either higher or lower, is the_____.

6. A

6. [bass clef note] is_____.

7. g^{ii}

7. [treble clef note] is_____.

8. c^i

8. [alto clef note] is_____.

9. d

9. [alto clef note] is_____.

10. f

10. [bass clef note] is_____.

STUDIES

1. Indicate the proper pitch and octave designations.

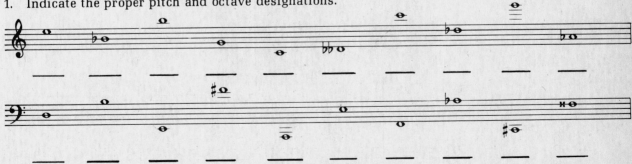

SCALES: Major and Minor

Major and minor scales are formed primarily from *half-steps (semi-tones)* and *whole steps (whole tones)*. The semi-tone is the smallest interval utilized in the equal-temperament system.

An octave segment of a piano keyboard provides an excellent graph of the arrangement of whole tones and semi-tones. Immediately adjacent notes are semi-tones (half-steps):

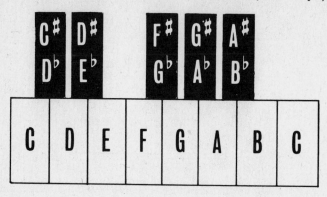

The following are semi-tones:

C to C♯(D♭)
D to D♯(E♭)
E to F
F to F♯(G♭)
G to G♯(A♭)
A to A♯(B♭)
B to C

Whole tones consist of *two* semi-tones:

C to D
C♯ to D♯
E to F♯
A to B etc.

Intervals (the distance between two pitches) are discussed in Chapter 5. At this point of investigation, the white notes of the keyboard will provide a frame of reference and basic terminology:

C *ascending* to D is a second

C *ascending* to E is a third

C *ascending* to F is a fourth

C *ascending* to G is a fifth

C *ascending* to A is a sixth

C *ascending* to B is a seventh

C *ascending* to C is an octave

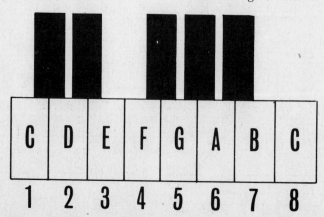

CONSTRUCTION OF MAJOR AND MINOR SCALES

Major and minor scales are shown below. All half-steps are marked by (∧). Observe the tone *plus* semitone between scale degrees 6 and 7 in the *harmonic minor* scale.

MAJOR SCALE

NAMES OF SCALE DEGREES (STEPS)

1. Tonic	4. Subdominant
2. Supertonic	5. Dominant
3. Mediant	6. Submediant
	7. Leading tone

MINOR SCALES

Natural Minor:

Harmonic Minor:

Melodic Minor:

PROGRAM V

PENTATONIC AND SYNTHETIC SCALES

1. NO RESPONSE

1. In addition to the diatonic scale, there are numerous other scales found in music. One of these is the *pentatonic scale,* which consists of five tones within the range of an octave.

2. FIVE

2. The word "pentatonic," derived from the Greek word *pente* ("five"), refers to the _____ tones that make up the pentatonic scale.

3. ORIENTAL

3. Because any five-note division of the octave is a pentatonic scale, there are numerous types of pentatonic scales. One of these, associated especially with Oriental music and used by Impressionist composers, is the anhemitonic pentatonic scale. Another name for this scale is "Chinese" pentatonic scale because of its association with _____ music.

4. c♯ d♯ f♯ g♯ a♯ (c♯^{i})

4. The Chinese pentatonic scale contains three whole steps, three minor thirds, and no semi-tones. It can be produced on the piano by playing the five black keys in ascending order. Construct a pentatonic scale beginning on c♯:

   c♯ ____ ____ ____ ____ (c♯ ^{i})

5. c d f g a (c^i)

5. Using the above example, construct a pentatonic scale beginning on c:

   c ____ ____ ____ ____ (c^i)

6. f♯ g♯ a♯ c♯^{i} d♯^{i} (f♯^{i})

6. Construct a pentatonic scale on f♯, using only the black notes of a piano:

   f♯ ____ ____ ____ ____ ( )

7. NO RESPONSE

7. The pentatonic scale may be derived from the projection of equidistant intervals.

8. SYNTHETIC

8. A final category of scales appearing in Western music (besides the diatonic, chromatic, and pentatonic scales) is that of the *synthetic scales.* These invented scales can be used as the basis for a melodic and harmonic vocabulary. Four types of scales that are used in Western music are the diatonic, chromatic, pentatonic, and _____ scales.

9. e f$\sharp$ g$\sharp$ a$\sharp$ c^i d^i e^i

9. One type of synthetic scale is the *whole-tone scale*, which is without semi-tones. An example is:

c d e f$\sharp$ g$\sharp$ a$\sharp$ c^i

Construct a whole-tone scale beginning on e:

e — — — — — —

10. b

10. Another type of synthetic scale is the *gypsy* or *Hungarian scale*. An example is:

c d e$\flat$ f$\sharp$ g a$\flat$ b c^i

Which of the following is a Gypsy scale?

a. g a b$\flat$ c^i d^i e$\flat^i$ f$\sharp^i$ g^i

b. g a b$\flat$ c$\sharp^i$ d^i e$\flat^i$ f$\sharp^i$ g^i

11. g a$\flat$ b$\flat$ b$\natural$ c$\sharp^i$
d$_i$ e^i f^i g^i

11. A third type of synthetic scale consists of the alternation of half and whole steps (*semi-tone-tone scale*):

c d$\flat$ e$\flat$ e$\natural$ f$\sharp$ g a b$\flat$ c^i

Construct a scale that alternates semi-tones with tones, beginning on g:

g — — — — — — — —

12. PENTATONIC
SCALE

12. What type of scale is the following?

f g a c^i d^i

13. d e f$\sharp$ g$\sharp$ a$\sharp$ c^i d^i

13. Add accidentals to the following to form a whole-tone scale beginning on d:

d e f g a c^i d^i

14. SEMI-TONE—TONE,
SYNTHETIC

14. The _____-_____-_____ scale, one of the _____ scales, consists of the alternation of half and whole steps.

15. d e f g a$\flat$ b$\flat$
b$\natural$ c$\sharp^i$ d^i

15. Construct a scale that consists of the alternation of whole and half steps beginning on d:

d — — — — — — — —

PROGRAM VI

INTERVALS

1. NO RESPONSE

    1. An *interval* is the distance between two pitches.

2. INTERVAL

    2. There are two main varieties of intervals, differentiated by the manner in which the two pitches are to be sounded. If they are written to sound simultaneously, they are said to comprise an *harmonic interval*. If they are to be sounded successively, a *melodic interval* is formed. The terms *harmonic* and *melodic* indicate the method by which the two pitches of the _____ are to be sounded.

3. MELODIC

    3. If the two pitches are to be sounded successively, the interval is termed _____ .

4. SIMULTANEOUSLY

    4. Harmonic intervals occur when two pitches are to sound _____ .

5. INTERVALS

    5. _____ measure the distance between two pitches. This measurement is defined numerically and is found by counting the number of pitch degrees encompassed by the interval. Observe in the example below that the two pitch degrees comprising the interval are included in the computation:

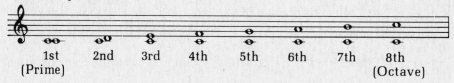

1st   2nd   3rd   4th   5th   6th   7th   8th

(Prime)   (Octave)

6. NO RESPONSE

    6. In the diagram in the preceding frame, all of the intervals have been labeled numerically. Note, however, that there are special names for the interval of the first and for the interval of the eighth. The interval of the first is labeled *prime* (or *unison*), the interval of the eighth is labeled *octave* (or *8ve*).

7. OCTAVES

    7. All of the following intervals are _____ .

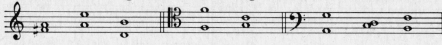

8. THIRD, FIFTH,
SIXTH; OCTAVE,
FOURTH; SEVENTH,
SECOND, FIFTH

    8. Label the following intervals according to their numerical content:

___   ___   ___   ___   ___   ___   ___   ___

9. HARMONIC

    9. All of the intervals in frame 8 are:

          Harmonic   Melodic   (circle one)

10. SUCCESSIVELY

    10. For the intervals in frame 8 to be termed *melodic*, each of the groups of two pitches would have to be written so that they would sound _____ , thus:

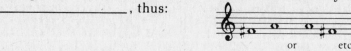

              or   etc.

11. DO NOT

11. Note that in the example in frame 10 the inclusion of the accidental (#) does not affect the numerical content of the interval. (Accidentals will be of importance later when a discussion of the *quality* of intervals is undertaken.) Accidentals do/do not (circle one) affect the numerical content of intervals.

12. FIFTH, THIRD, SEVENTH; FOURTH, SIXTH

12. Label the following intervals according to numerical content:

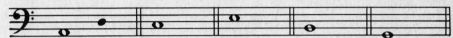

_____ _____ _____ _____ _____

13. MELODIC, SUCCESSIVELY

13. The intervals in frame 12 are of the _____ variety because they are to be sounded _____.

14.

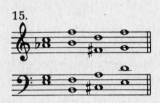

14. Write melodic intervals of the fourth for each of the following pitches:

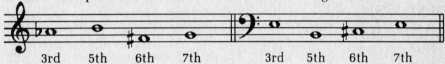

15.

15. Write the specified harmonic intervals above the given notes:

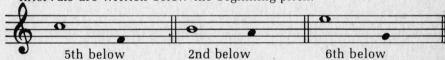

3rd   5th   6th   7th   3rd   5th   6th   7th

16. NO RESPONSE

16. Intervals may also be calculated by counting downward. The following intervals are written *below* the beginning pitch.

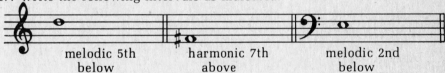

5th below   2nd below   6th below

17.

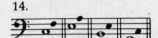

17. Write the following intervals as indicated:

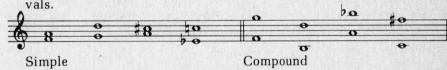

melodic 5th   harmonic 7th   melodic 2nd
below   above   below

18. NO

18. Do accidentals affect the numerical content of intervals? _____ (yes/no)

19. NO RESPONSE

19. All intervals whose distance is no greater than the octave are called *simple* intervals. Intervals that exceed the octave are called *compound* intervals.

Simple   Compound

20. SIMPLE; COMPOUND

20. Intervals that are no greater than the octave (including the octave) are termed _____; intervals that exceed the span of the octave, _____.

21. SIM., SIM., SIM.;
COM., SIM., SIM.;
COM., SIM.

21. Determine which of the following intervals are simple and which are compound. Label them accordingly (as SIM. or COM.).

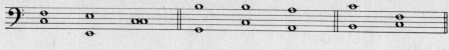

___ ___ ___   ___ ___ ___   ___ ___

22.

22. Write the following intervals:

HARMONIC:

5th above   3rd below   9th below   6th below

MELODIC:

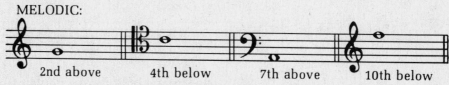

2nd above   4th below   7th above   10th below

23. NO RESPONSE

23. *Consonant* and *dissonant* are terms used to describe intervals. (The terms refer to the traditional grouping of intervals—and of all sounds—according to the ear's ability to grasp them.) All intervals are termed *consonant* except seconds, sevenths, and the tritone.

24. CONSONANT;
CONSONANT;
DISSONANT

24. Fourths are described as being _____ .
Sixths are described as being _____ :
Seconds are described as being _____ :

25. THIRDS, SIXTHS

25. The class of intervals that is described as consonant (primes, thirds, fourths, fifths, sixths, octaves) is subdivided into *perfect consonants* and *imperfect consonants*. The perfect consonants are primes, fourths, fifths, and octaves. The imperfect consonants are _____ and _____ .

26. CONSONANT,
DISSONANT

26. All intervals can be described as being either _____ or _____ .

27. PRIMES, FOURTHS,
FIFTHS, OCTAVES

27. The perfect consonants are _____ , _____ . _____ , and _____ .

28. IMPERFECT
CONSONANTS

28. Thirds and sixths are _____ _____ .

29. SECONDS,
SEVENTHS

29. The dissonant intervals are typically _____ and _____ .

30. PC, D, IC, PC,
PC, IC, D, PC

30. Label the following intervals as dissonants (D), imperfect consonants (IC), or perfect consonants (PC):

___ ___ ___ ___ ___ ___ ___ ___

STUDIES

1. Intervals (refer to pp. 27–30 of text).

   Notate intervals above and below the given note, as indicated.

   a. *Above* the given note:

2. Triads (please refer to pp. 32–33 of text.)

   Notate triads as indicated.

   EXAMPLES:

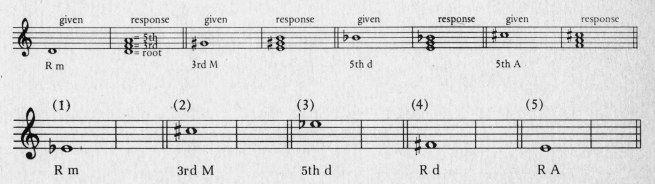

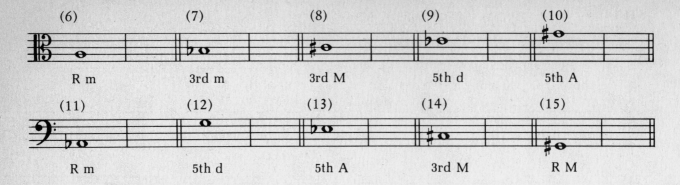

(6) R m   (7) 3rd m   (8) 3rd M   (9) 5th d   (10) 5th A

(11) R m   (12) 5th d   (13) 5th A   (14) 3rd M   (15) R M

3. Key signatures (refer to pp. 30–31 of text).

    a. Study the circle-of-fifths chart.

CIRCLE OF FIFTHS FOR KEY SIGNATURES

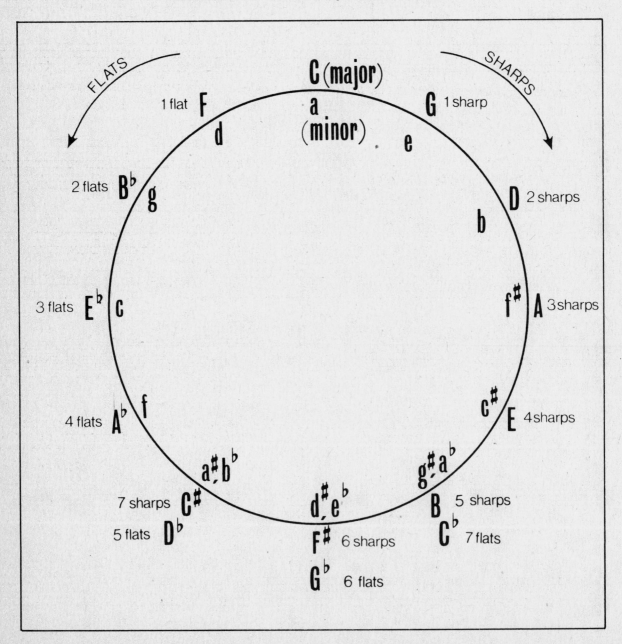

b.   Write key signatures for the following keys.

(1) e minor   (2) G♭ Major   (3) B Major

(4) f minor   (5) C♯ Major   (6) e♭ minor

(7) b minor   (8) G Major   (9) c minor

(10) A♭ Major   (11) g minor   (12) f♯ minor

Fundamentals Quizzes

It is suggested that each Fundamentals Quiz be taken within a prescribed time limit (10 to 12 minutes). It is further recommended that any student completing a given quiz with 100 percent accuracy be exempted from taking the subsequent ones.

FUNDAMENTALS QUIZ 1

I.   Write the following key signatures:

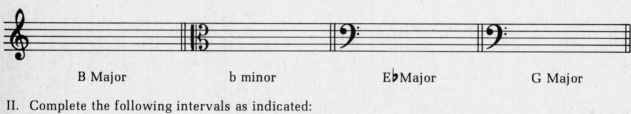

B Major   b minor   E♭ Major   G Major

II. Complete the following intervals as indicated:

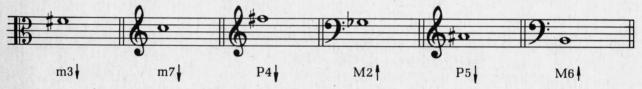

m3↓   m7↓   P4↓   M2↑   P5↓   M6↑

III. Write the following scales (ascending and descending):

F Major   Mixolydian

A♭ Major   e melodic minor

IV. Complete the following triads as indicated:

Root d   3rd M   Root m   5th m   3rd M   Root A

FUNDAMENTALS QUIZ 2

I. Write the following key signatures:

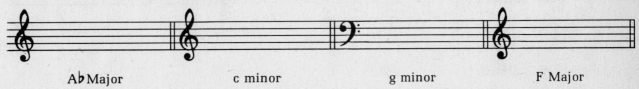

A♭ Major   c minor   g minor   F Major

II. Complete the following intervals as indicated:

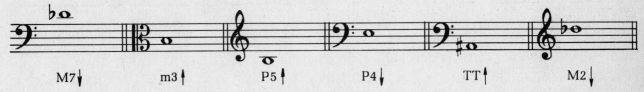

M7↓   m3↑   P5↑   P4↓   TT↑   M2↓

III. Write the following scales (ascending and descending):

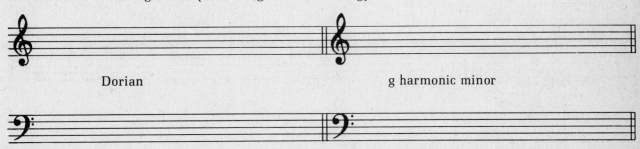

Dorian   g harmonic minor

A Major   B♭ Major

IV. Complete the following triads as indicated:

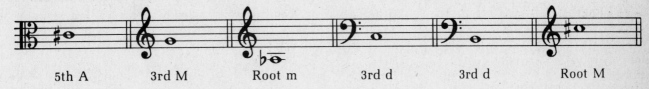

5th A   3rd M   Root m   3rd d   3rd d   Root M

FUNDAMENTALS QUIZ 3

I. Write the following key signatures:

d minor   E Major   c minor   A Major

II. Complete the following intervals as indicated:

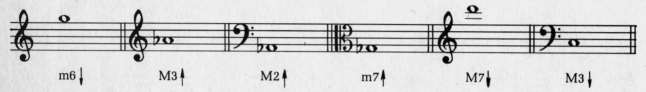

m6↓   M3↑   M2↑   m7↑   M7↓   M3↓

III. Write the following scales (ascending and descending):

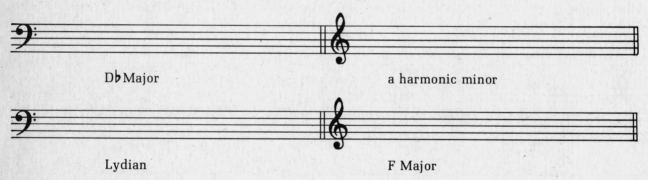

Db Major   a harmonic minor

Lydian   F Major

IV. Complete the following triads as indicated:

Root A   3rd d   5th d   Root m   3rd M   3rd M

FUNDAMENTALS QUIZ 4

I. Write the following key signatures:

D Major   B♭ Major   b minor   f# minor

II. Complete the following intervals as indicated:

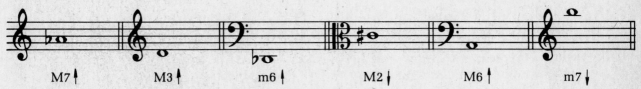

M7 ↑   M3 ↑   m6 ↑   M2 ↓   M6 ↑   m7 ↓

III. Write the following scales (ascending and descending):

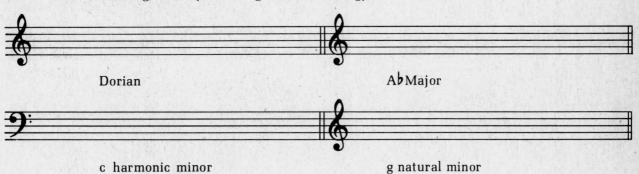

Dorian   A♭ Major

c harmonic minor   g natural minor

IV. Complete the following triads as indicated:

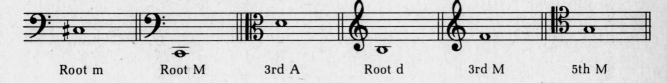

Root m   Root M   3rd A   Root d   3rd M   5th M

FUNDAMENTALS QUIZ 5

I. Write the following key signatures:

f minor   d minor   G♭ Major   b minor

II. Complete the following intervals as indicated:

M6 ↓   M6 ↑   m3 ↑   M2 ↓   M7 ↑   m7 ↓

III. Write the following scales (ascending and descending):

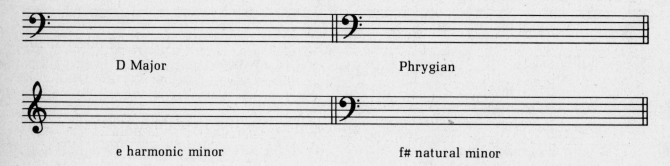

D Major   Phrygian

e harmonic minor   f# natural minor

IV. Complete the following triads as indicated:

Root d   Root M   3rd m   5th A   Root A   Root m

FUNDAMENTALS QUIZ 6

I. Write the following key signatures:

G Major   f minor   c minor   A♭ Major

II. Complete the following intervals as indicated:

M7↑   M3↓   m3↑   M2↓   m6↑   m7↓

III. Write the following scales (ascending and descending):

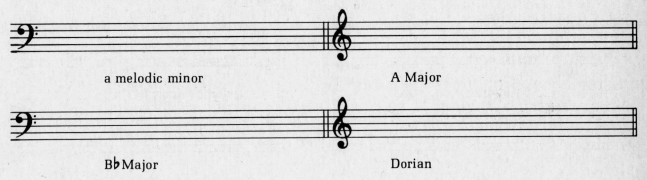

a melodic minor   A Major

B♭ Major   Dorian

IV. Complete the following triads as indicated:

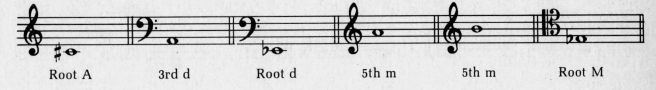

Root A   3rd d   Root d   5th m   5th m   Root M

FUNDAMENTALS QUIZ 7

I. Write the following key signatures:

Gb Major   c minor   g minor   F# Major

II. Complete the following intervals as indicated:

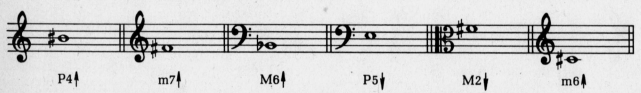

P4↑   m7↑   M6↑   P5↓   M2↓   m6↑

III. Write the following scales (ascending and descending):

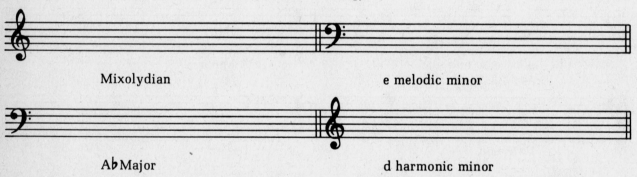

Mixolydian   e melodic minor

Ab Major   d harmonic minor

IV. Complete the following triads as indicated:

3rd A   5th M   Root m   3rd d   Root A   5th m

FUNDAMENTALS QUIZ 8

I.   Write the following key signatures:

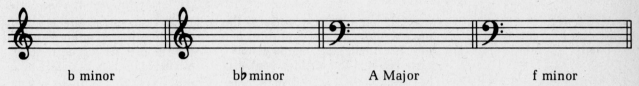

b minor   b♭ minor   A Major   f minor

II. Complete the following intervals as indicated:

m6 ↑   M3 ↑   m7 ↓   M2 ↓   m3 ↑   M6 ↓

III. Write the following scales (ascending and descending):

A♭ Major   G Major

b melodic minor   Lydian

IV. Complete the following triads as indicated:

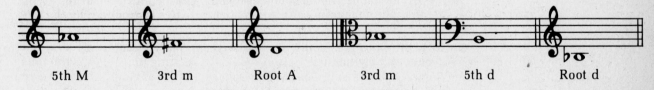

5th M   3rd m   Root A   3rd m   5th d   Root d

Chapter 4
PITCH ORGANIZATION

PROGRAM VII

MODES

1. OCTAVE

    1. *Mode*, in the broadest sense of the term, refers to the arrangement of tones within an octave. In this context, all scales (major, minor, whole-tone, invented, etc.) can be considered to be modes. As a generic term, *mode* denotes the arrangement of tones within an _____.

2. MIDDLE AGES, RENAISSANCE

    2. The pitch resources used in the common-practice period (c. 1600 to 1900) are generally called *scales*, while the term *mode* is applied to (a) the modes used in ancient Greek music and (b) the modes used in Western music during the Middle Ages and the Renaissance. The term *mode* is applied to the pitch resources used in ancient Greek music and those used in Western music during the _____ and _____.

3. DESCENDING

    3. Ancient Greek modes resulted from conjunct and disjunct tetrachords (four adjacent notes) in descending pitch order. The notes in Greek modes are arranged in _____ order.

4. DOCTRINE OF ETHOS

    4. In a view known as the doctrine of ethos, Greek modes were thought to have an effect on the character and state of mind of the listener and performer, in accordance with pitch placement and arrangement of whole tones and semi-tones. The view that Greek modes could affect the character and state of mind of a person is called the _____.

5. TERMINOLOGY

    5. Although similar in terminology, there is little correspondence between the Greek modes and the modes of Western Medieval and Renaissance music. Greek modes and early Western modes resemble each other in _____ , but have little else in common.

6. AMBITUS

    6. Most sacred melodies from the Middle Ages have a range, or *ambitus*, limited to an octave plus one or two notes. Play and sing the following modal melody. It has an ambitus of an octave plus one note.

    Another word for the range of a sacred Medieval melody is _____.

7. FINALIS

    7. In modal melodies, the tone that typically produces a concluding effect is called the *finalis*. Modal melodies usually end on (and often begin on) the finalis. The concluding effect in modal melodies is produced by the tone called the _____.

8.

Mode	Fin.	R.T.
dorian	d	a
phrygian	e	c
lydian	f	c
mixolydian	g	d
aeolian	a	e
ionian	c	g

    8. In addition to the finalis, modes have another characteristic tone that serves as a further delineation, called the *reciting tone* (also psalm tone, tenor, or dominant). The reciting tone is a fifth above the finalis. An exception is the phrygian mode, whose reciting tone is a sixth above the finalis. Complete the following chart:

Mode	Finalis	Reciting Tone
dorian	d	a
phrygian	e	c
lydian	____	____
mixolydian	____	____
aeolian	____	____
ionian	____	____

9. FOURTH

9. The six modes cited in frame 8 are called *authentic* modes. Each authentic mode has a corresponding *plagal* mode, which begins a fourth lower. Plagal modes are designated by the prefix "hypo." Plagal modes begin a _____ lower than their corresponding authentic mode.

10. NO RESPONSE

10. As an example, the lydian mode and its corresponding plagal mode, hypolydian, are given below.

Lydian (authentic)   Hypolydian (plagal)

11.

11. The mixolydian mode is given below. Write its corresponding plagal mode (hypomixolydian) and indicate the whole tones and semi-tones of each.

Mixolydian   Hypomixolydian

12. d

12. The finalis of a plagal mode is the same note as the finalis of its corresponding authentic mode. For example, a is the finalis of the aeolian *and* hypoaeolian modes. The finalis of the dorian mode is d. What is the finalis of the hypodorian mode? _____

13.

13. Write the finalis for the hypophrygian, hypolydian, hypomixolydian, and hypoionian modes. (You may refer to frame 8.)

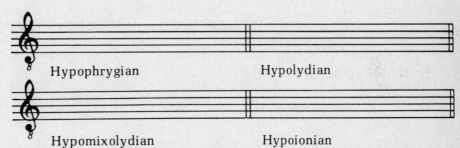

Hypophrygian   Hypolydian

Hypomixolydian   Hypoionian

14. A THIRD ABOVE

14. The reciting tone of the authentic modes (except phrygian) is a fifth above the finalis, but the reciting tone of the plagal modes is generally a third above it. Generally, the reciting tone of the plagal modes is _____ _____ the finalis.

15.

Mode	Fin.	R.T.
dorian	d	a
hypodorian	**d**	**f**
lydian	f	c
hypolydian	f	a
aeolian	a	e
hypoaeolian	a	c

15. Based on the information given in frame 14, complete the following chart:

Mode	Finalis	Reciting Tone
dorian	d	a
hypodorian	d	f
lydian	___	___
hypolydian	___	___
aeolian	___	___
hypoaeolian	___	___

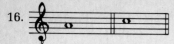

16. Two plagal modes do not have their reciting tone a third above the finalis. The reciting tone of hypophrygian is a (not g), and the reciting tone of hypomixolydian is c (not b). Write the reciting tone for hypophrygian and hypomixolydian modes:

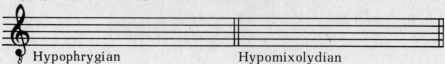

Hypophrygian　　　　　　　Hypomixolydian

17. NO RESPONSE

17. The following chart shows the finalis, reciting tone, and ambitus of each of the modes.

| I | II | III | IV |
| dorian | hypodorian | phrygian | hypophrygian |

| V | VI | VII | VIII |
| lydian | hypolydian | mixolydian | hypomixolydian |

| IX | X | XI | XII |
| aeolian | hypoaeolian | ionian | hypoionian |

o = finalis　　　 = dominant　　　 = range (ambitus)
　　　　　　　　(reciting tone)

18. AEOLIAN,
HYPOAEOLIAN,
IONIAN,
HYPOIONIAN

18. While all twelve of the above modes were used in Medieval secular music, only modes I—VIII were considered proper for use in church music. These modes were, and still are, designated as "church modes." The modes not considered proper for church music were _____ , _____ , _____ , and _____ .

19. LOCRIAN,
HYPOLOCRIAN

19. There are authentic modes beginning on d, e, f, g, a, and c. An authentic mode beginning on b (locrian) and its corresponding plagal mode (hypolocrian) are possible, but are rarely used because they involve a tritone between the finalis and the fifth pitch above it. These two modes are considered essentially theoretical modes. The theoretical authentic mode on b is _____ and its corresponding plagal mode is _____ _____ .

20. NATURAL MINOR,
MAJOR

20. The Medieval modes, resulting from classification of Medieval chant or plainsong melodies, were the basis of Medieval music (monophonic and polyphonic) and were used throughout the Renaissance. Two of the modes remained in use and became the basis of the major-minor scale system: the aeolian mode has the same arrangement of whole and semitones as the natural minor scale, and the ionian mode the same internal pitch order as the major scale. The aeolian and ionian modes form the basis of the _____ scale and the _____ scale, respectively.

PROGRAM VIII

HEXACHORDS

1.

1. The term *hexachord* (from the Greek word *hexa*, six; *chordos*, tone, string) refers to a six-note pattern. Such a pattern, beginning on middle c, would be:

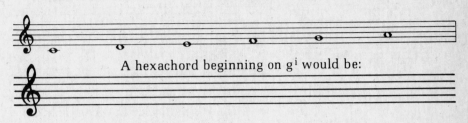

A hexachord beginning on g^i would be:

2. HEXACHORDS,
   GUIDO D'AREZZO

2. In the eleventh century Guido D'Arezzo developed the Medieval hexachord system. A system of six-note patterns, called _____, was developed in the eleventh century by _____.

3. G to e^{ii}, SEVEN

3. Guido's system consisted of seven overlapping hexachords. These hexachords, extended and overlapping, spanned the entire Medieval *gamut* (range), which was G—e^{ii}.

The Medieval gamut, which extended from ____ to ____, was spanned by a system of _____ overlapping hexachords.

4. IN THE MIDDLE

4. Each of the hexachords used in Guido's system was based on a pattern of whole steps (tones) and half-steps (semi-tones). These are usually abbreviated T (tone) and S (semi-tone). Guido's hexachord pattern was the following: TTSTT.

Where was the half-step located in Guido's hexachord pattern? _____.

5.

5. With this sign ∧ mark the S in the G hexachord:

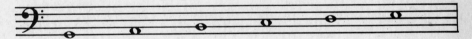

6. THREE; G, C, and F;
   TTSTT

6. There are three different kinds of hexachords used in Guido's system. These hexachords begin on G, C, and F. Guido used _____ different kinds of hexachords in his system. They began on the notes __, __, and __. They all kept the same tone and semi-tone pattern, which is _____.

7. a. NATURALE

b. MOLLE (SOFT)

c. DURUM (HARD)

7. The C hexachord is called the *naturale* hexachord; it contains no B. The F hexachord is called the *molle* (soft) hexachord; it contains a B♭. The G hexachord is called the *durum* (hard) hexachord; it contains a B♮.

a. There is no B in the C hexachord, which is called the _____ hexachord. It is written:

b. The F hexachord, which is called the _____ hexachord, contains a B♭. It is written:

c. The B is natural in the G hexachord, which is called the _____ hexachord. It is written:

8. TTSTT

8. All three of the hexachords of Guido have the same pattern of tones and semi-tones, which is _____.

9. THREE; G, C, and F; DURUM (HARD), NATURALE, MOLLE (SOFT)

9. In his hexachord system Guido used _____ different kinds of hexachords. They began on the notes ___ , ___ , and ___ ; and they were called (respectively) _____ , _____ , and _____.

10. TTSTT; UT-RE-MI-FA-SOL-LA; MI and FA

10. Guido used the hexachord system as a way to teach singing with syllables. Therefore, each of the hexachords employed the syllables UT-RE-MI-FA-SOL-LA. The *molle* (F) hexachord, with syllables, was:

ut   re   mi   fa   sol   la

Since all the hexachords had the same _____ pattern, and all the hexachords used the syllables _____ , the semi-tone (S) was always between the syllables _____ and _____.

11. f FA UT; g SOL RE UT

11. Since the hexachords overlapped, most notes had two or three syllables under them.

ut   re   mi   fa   sol   la   etc.
                        ut   re   mi   fa   sol
                                                ut   re
                                                        ut

When not sung, these notes were called by their letter name plus the syllables underneath them. For example, c would be called c *fa ut*. f would be called _____ . g would be called _____ .

12. G to e^ii; SEVEN; THREE; C, F, and G

12. Guido d'Arezzo's hexachord system spanned the Medieval gamut, _____ to _____, by a series of _____ overlapping hexachords. These hexachords were of _____ different kinds and began on the notes ___ , ___ , and ___ .

13. NATURALE, MOLLE, and DURUM

13. The names of the three different kinds of hexachords were (on C, F, and G, respectively): _____ , _____ , and _____ .

14. MUTATION

14. Since the hexachords overlap, a musical composition could move from one hexachord to another so as not to be confined within a six-note span. This movement was called *modulation,* or by the Medieval term *mutation.* The Medieval practice of _____ provided for the movement from one hexachord to another.

15. FLAT;
    NATURAL; NO

15. In the *molle* (F) hexachord, the B is _____ . In the *durum* (G) hexachord, the B is _____ . In the *naturale* (C) hexachord, there is _____ B.

16. FLAT

16. If a composition begins in the C hexachord and needs to go *above* its six-note pattern, it may *mutate* to the next hexachord in line—the F hexachord. To do this, the rule of the F hexachord must be followed. The rule of the F hexachord dictates that the B must be _____ .

17. C, F

17. An example of the above case is the following:

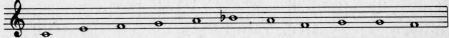

This example shows a composition mutating from the ____ hexachord to the _____ hexachord.

PROGRAM IX

SOLMIZATION

1. SOLMIZATION

1. In *solmization*, pitches are sung to syllable rather than letter names of notes. The system used when singing a melody to syllable names is called _____.

2. HYMN TO ST. JOHN

2. The *Hymn to St. John*, quoted in the eleventh century by Guido d'Arezzo, is an early source from which solmization is derived. Sight singing to syllables is derived from the _____ __ __ _____ .

3. FIRST NOTE

3. The first note of each of the first six phrases of this hymn is successively higher. A gradually ascending line is produced by the successively higher pitch of the _____ _____ of each of the first six phrases.

4. NO RESPONSE

4. The downward direction of the final line forms a satisfying total melodic shape for the hymn. When the melodic curve rises to a high point, then descends, the melody may be described as *curvilinear*.

5. DOWNWARD

5. The melodic direction of the last line of the hymn is _____ .

6. CURVILINEAR

6. The word _____ could be used to describe the total shape of the melody.

7. FIRST SYLLABLE

7. Guido's system used the first syllable of each phrase of the *Hymn to St. John* as the basis of solmization. The syllables of solmization are derived from the _____ _____ of each successive line of text.

8. SI, TI

8. The seventh syllable, originally called *si* (also called *ti*) was added c. 1650 and was formed from the initial letters of the words *Sancte Joannes*. The original name of the seventh syllable is _____ or _____ .

9. DO, UT

9. The original name for the first syllable, *ut*, has been changed to *do* (e.g., in English and Italian). The syllables in use today are *do, re, mi, fa, sol, la, ti, (do)*, not including chromatic alterations. Today, the first syllable of solmization is _____, although it was originally known as _____ .

10. NO RESPONSE

10. There are two systems of solmization in use today. In the *fixed-do* system, the syllable name is invariable for any note of a given letter name, while in the *moveable-do* system the *tonic* note is always called *do*.

11. TONIC

11. *Do* is the syllable name given to the _____ in the moveable-*do* system.

12. FIXED-DO

12.

A:
This note would be *la* in the _____ - ____ system.

13. MOVEABLE-DO

13.

E♭:
This note would be *do* in the _____ - ____ system.

14. a. LA DO FA
    RE SOL LA
  b. DO MI LA
    FA TI DO

14. Write syllable names under the notes of the following passage, using both systems of solmization:

a. ___ ___ ___ ___ ___ ___ (fixed)
b. ___ ___ ___ ___ ___ ___ (move.)

15. FA, SOL, RE, LA, DO

15. When chromatic inflections are used to raise a note, the vowel sound of the corresponding syllable is narrowed. Thus, the syllables become *di, ri, fi, si, li.*

fi is the raised form of _____
si is the raised form of _____
ri is the raised form of _____
li is the raised form of _____
di is the raised form of _____

16. SOL, MI, LA, RE, TI

16. When chromatic inflections are used to lower a note, the vowel sound of the corresponding syllable is broadened and the syllables become *te, le, se, me, ra.*

se is the lowered form of _____
me is the lowered form of _____
le is the lowered form of _____
ra is the lowered form of _____
te is the lowered form of _____

17. NO RESPONSE

17. Frames 15 and 16 refer to the moveable-*do* system as applied to chromatic inflections in a major key. In a minor key, either of two methods of syllable naming may be used: (a) using *la* as the tonic and continuing *ti, do,* etc.; or (b) using *do* as the tonic and continuing *re, me,* etc.[1]

18 a. LA FA DO MI
    FI SI LA
  b. DO LE ME SOL
    LA TI DO

18. Write the syllable names under the notes of the following passage, using both methods (a) and (b) of frame 17:

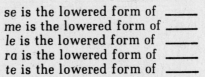

a. ___ ___ ___ ___ ___ ___
b. ___ ___ ___ ___ ___ ___

19. NO RESPONSE

19. A memory aid for chromatic inflections is shown in the following ladder:

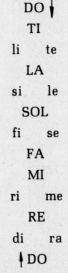

DO ↓
TI
li   te
LA
si   le
SOL
fi   se
FA
MI
ri   me
RE
di   ra
↑ DO

[1]Please also see Willi Apel, *Harvard Dictionary of Music*, 2nd Edition, pp. 786–787 for a different version of inflections.

STUDIES

Solmization.

a. Write the syllable names above notes of these examples, using the moveable-*do* system.

(1) Soprano of a Wilbye madrigal — 1598

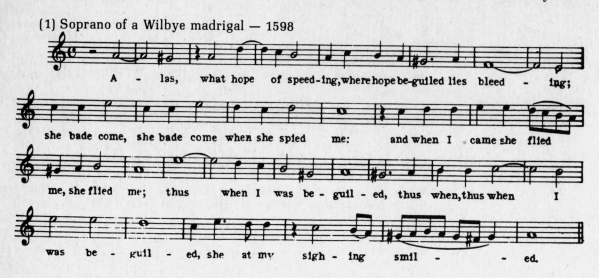

(2) Final part of Brahms' song "Wie Melodien"

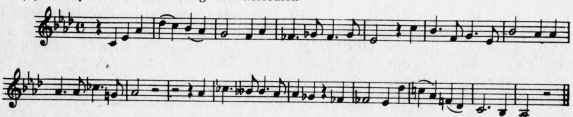

b. Notate "My Country 'tis of Thee" in the key of E Major. Write syllable names under each note using moveable-*do* system.

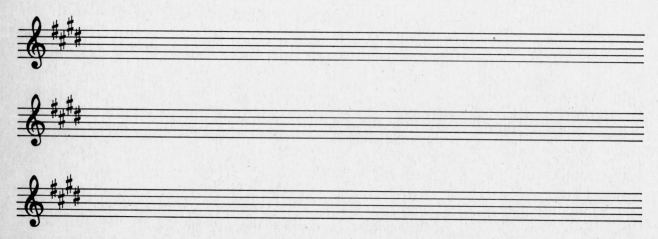

PROGRAM X

TEMPERAMENT

1. PYTHAGOREAN

    1. The term *temperament* refers to various tuning systems for the subdivision of the octave. The Pythagorean system uses the pure fifth as the basis of interval derivation. The acoustically correct "pure" fifth is employed in the _____ system.

2. PURE THIRD

    2. Just intonation utilizes pure fifths (as in the Pythagorean system) and a *pure third*: c g d^i a^i e^{ii} (pure). The difference, then, between the Pythagorean and just intonation systems is that just intonation uses a _____ _____ .

3. FALSE

    3. The mean-tone system was used c. 1500. The system is based on a smaller fifth (697, instead of 702 cents). A succession of smaller fifths, c g d^i a^i e^{ii}, produces a pure third (e^{ii}). Mean-tone tuning uses two kinds of fifths (true/false). _____ .

4. TWELVE EQUAL
    PARTS

    4. Equal temperament divides the octave into twelve equal parts. Intervals other than the octave, therefore, deviate from the acoustically correct ratios of the Pythagorean system. Division of the octave into _____ _____ _____ constitutes the basis of equal temperament.

5. TUNING

    5. Temperament is a term for _____ systems.

6. OCTAVE

    6. The twelve different pitches comprised by equal temperament are all contained within one _____ .

7. e^{ii}

    7. Just intonation uses pure fifths and a pure third. In the series c g d^i a^i e^{ii}, which pitch is pure? _____

8. FIFTH

    8. In the Pythagorean system, tones are derived from the interval of a pure _____ .

9. MEAN-TONE

    9. A system which uses a succession of smaller fifths is called _____ _____ .

10. EQUAL
    TEMPERAMENT

    10. _____ _____ is the basis of most Western music performed or written today.

Chapter 5
ELEMENTS OF MUSIC: RHYTHM

STUDIES

1. Practice tapping the following rhythmic exercises. Use a metronome, progressing from ♪ = 60 to ♩. = 120.

a.

b.

c.

d.

e. Two-voice canon

From Peter Phillips, *The Rhythm Book.* ©Copyright 1971 by Associated Music Publishers, Inc. Used by permission.

2. Practice tapping the following rhythmic exercises. Keep a steady tempo. Use a metronome, progressing from ♪ = c. 60 to ♩ = c. 120.

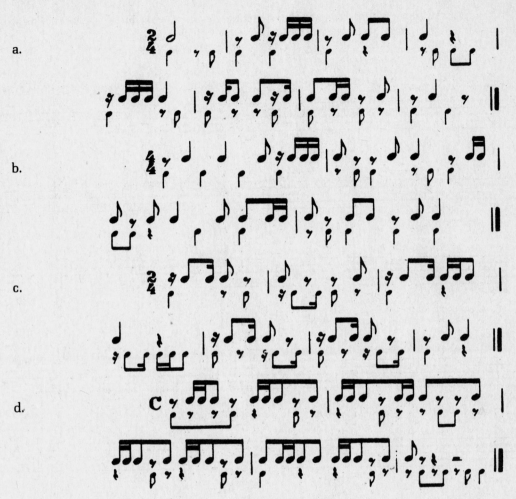

More difficult:

3. Compose a short percussion piece.

a. Analyze the rhythmic patterns in the first two measures for unity and variety of rhythmic gesture.

b. Continue the composition for about ten measures through the use of similar rhythmic development techniques.

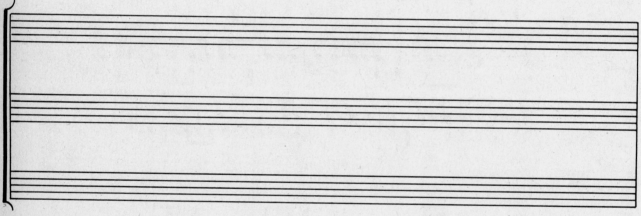

4. In the spaces provided below draw the following conducting patterns.

a. 6
    8

b. 3
    4

c. 4
    8

d. 5
    4

e. 7
    8

f. 8
    8

5. Writing rhythmic devices.

   a. Write a melody that illustrates the dynamic, tonic, and agogic accents.

   b. Demonstrate a rhythmic syncopation.

   c. Write an example of hemiola.

   d. Write a short example using the device of polyrhythm.

6. Definitions.
   Briefly but clearly identify or define the following terms and concepts.

   a. Metrical rhythm:

   b. Compound meter:

   c. Borrowed division:

   d. Agogic accent:

   e. Hemiola:

   f. Polyrhythm:

   g. Isorhythm:

   h. Motor rhythm:

   i. Anacrusis:

Chapter 6
ELEMENTS OF MUSIC: MELODY

STUDIES

1. Melodic Analysis.

    Respond to the directions or questions that relate to each of the melodies below.

    a. Ockeghem

Chanson Melody, *Ma maîtresse*, Johannes Ockeghem

He - las de vous bien plain - dre me de - vroi - e, s'il

ne vous plaist que brief - ment vous re - voy - e

(1) What are the modal/tonal characteristics?

(2) What is the proportion between conjunct and disjunct motion?

(3) Mark the primary high point and the primary low points.

(4) What pitch has the greatest emphasis in measures 1—5? Please explain your answer.

b. Bach

Organ Fugue Subject, J. S. Bach

BWV 564

(1) What is the relationship of measures 3 and 5 to measure 1? What is the term for this particular kind of treatment?

(2) What is the derivation of the material in measures 7 and 8?

(3) Briefly describe the function of the pitch d^{ii} in measures 7 and 8.

(4) What unusual rhythmic aspects are found? What kind of effect (or mood) is engendered by rhythmic means?

c. Beethoven

First Movement from Sonata Op. 57, Ludwig van Beethoven

(1) Briefly compare version (a) to version (b).

(2) Describe the balance of conjunct and disjunct motion in version (a).

d. Vaughan Williams

Hymn Tune, *Sine nomine*, Vaughan Williams

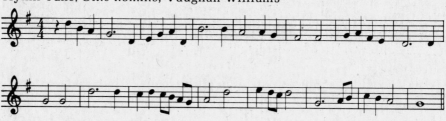

Used by permission of G. Schirmer, Inc.

(1) Describe the function of the pitch d^{ii} in this example.

(2) Circle all dotted half notes (♩.). What observation can be made?

(3) Mark appropriate phrases for purposes of singing (i.e., where should breaths be taken?).

2. Using the following fugue subject, illustrate the devices of inversion, retrograde, and augmentation.

J.S. Bach

3. Write a short, original two-part canon. The style may be of any historical period, but it should be consistent throughout.

4. Discussion of the *Invention 1* in C Major by J. S. Bach (text pp. 94–95).

   a. The subject first appears in bar_____ .

   b. Each successive pitch of the subject follows a _____ progression.

   c. The answer first appears in measure_____ and is_____.

   d. An inversion of the subject appears first in measure_____.

   e. The key at measure 15 is_____.

   f. A suggestion of augmentation of the subject appears in measure_____.

   g. The mirror or inversion of the subject is sequenced starting at measure_____.

ANSWERS (4): (a) 1 (b) major (c) 1, an octave lower (d) 3 (e) a minor (f) 3 (g) 9

5. Definitions.
   Define the following terms briefly and clearly.

   a. Dramatic shape:

   b. Types of melodic motion:

   c. Melodic gravity:

   d. Pitch coils:

   e. Motive (compare with cell and figure):

   f. Subject and theme:

   g. Phrase and period:

   h. *Cantus firmus*:

   i. Fugue:

   j. Invention:

6. Analyze the following two-voice motet.

 a. Determine the distance of all intervals.

 b. Examine the extent and kinds of imitation.

 c. Mark each cadence.

Expandi Manus (from the seventh Penitential Psalm), Orlandus Lassus

Chapters 1 – 6

REVIEW

1. Aesthetics is the philosophy or study of the beautiful. Two principal aesthetic views of music are that music is an _____ art and that it is an _____ art.

2. Boethius, a Roman statesman and philosopher of the sixth century, made the following three divisions of music: _____ , _____ , and _____ .

3. Sound is the phenomenon that is studied in the science of _____ .

4. Frequency refers to the number of _____ per second effected by an elastic body when the equilibrium of this body is disturbed. A subjective term used to describe this same phenomenon is _____ .

5. The amount of energy producing the vibrational disturbance, which is subjectively referred to as "soft" or "loud," is _____ .

6. The quality or color of a sound is called _____ and is determined by the number and relative intensity of its _____ .

7. The basic elements of music are: _____ , _____ , _____ , and _____ .

8. Notation represents the visual image of sound placement. A _____ or _____ refers to the five horizontal lines upon or between which the notes and rests are placed.

9. Clefs indicate the location on the staff of a particular pitch. The clefs most commonly used today are the (letter name) _____ , _____ , and _____ clefs.

10. Two types of notation that were developed in the Middle Ages were _____ and _____ notation. Common or standard notation in use today is derived from _____ notation.

11. Label the following pitches according to their correct octave placement:

12. _____ refers to the various tuning systems for the subdivision of the octave. The four systems that have been used in the course of music history are _____ , _____ , _____ , and _____ .

13. The three types of minor scales are _____ , _____ , and _____ .

14. The pentatonic scale, also widely used, is based on the projection of equidistant intervals. Illustrate a pentatonic scale above the following note:

15. Medieval church modes are classified according to three criteria: _____, _____, and _____ .

16. The Medieval modes are divided into authentic and plagal modes. One difference between these two types is that the ambitus of a plagal mode is a _____ lower than that of the corresponding authentic mode.

17. The hexachords of Medieval theory comprised six diatonic tones. There were three such hexachords:

_____ built on (pitch) _____

_____ built on (pitch) _____

_____ built on (pitch) _____, which contains a B♭

18. The distance between two pitches is called an _____ .

19. Three classes of intervals are _____ , _____, and _____ .

20. Any interval larger than an octave is termed _____ ; those within the octave are termed _____ .

21. An essential principle in the determining of an interval inversion is that the _____ of the ascending and descending intervals equals _____ .

22. When an interval is inverted, perfect remains _____ ; augmented becomes _____ ; major becomes _____ ; minor becomes _____ ; and diminished becomes _____ .

23. The term for three tones sounding simultaneously is _____ .

24. The four species of triads that are the basis of tertian music are _____ , _____ , _____ , and _____ .

25. Minor scales are of two categories, _____ or _____, as determined by their relationship to the _____ .

26. The three common minor scales are _____ , _____, and _____ .

27. The five common types of harmonic cadences are _____ , _____ , _____ , _____ , and _____ .

28. _____ refers to music systems which, for sight-singing purposes, designate notes by syllable rather than by letter names.

29. The two main systems of sight singing in current practice are the _____ and the _____ systems.

3. Transcribe the vocal line of Franz Schubert's *Mit dem grünen Lautenbande* for clarinet in B♭.

knüpf ich's ab und send es dir: Nun   hab   das Grü - ne   gern,____ nun
grün der Hoff-nung Fer-nen blühn,   drum   ha - ben wir es   gern,____ drum
weiss ich, wo die Lie-be thront,   dann   hab ich's Grün erst   gern,____ dann

hab   das Grü - ne   gern!
ha - ben wir es   gern.   fine
hab ich's Grün erst   gern.

fine

4. Transcribe the following trio movement for clarinet (B♭), viola, and French horn (F). The original is for violin, viola, and cello. Observe change of clef in measure 9.

From *Seven Paragraphs* (1925), Henry Cowell

VII.

Quasi andante

Chapter 8
COMBINATION OF ELEMENTS: TEXTURE, MUSICAL SYNTHESIS (FORM IN MUSIC)

STUDIES

1. Definitions.
   Define the following terms, which relate to *texture* in music.

   a. Monophony:

   b. Polyphony:

   c. Homophony:

   d. Heterophony:

   e. Alberti bass:

   f. "Third dimension":

2. Discuss the following items relating to the excerpt from Hassler's motet *Laudate Dominum*.

a. Write the *subject* of Choir I.

b. Briefly discuss the kind of imitation observed in the motet.

c. What aspects of performance practice are suggested in measures 14—16?

d. What is the role of texture in this motet excerpt? Of spatial organization?

Polychoral motet, *Laudate Dominum,* Hans Leo Hassler

2. Discussion of Robert Schumann's *Romance* from *Faschingsschwank*.

    a. Discuss the basic form of the *Romance*.

        (1) Which of the following is the phrase structure?

                a a b a,

                a b c a, or

                a a b c a

        (2) What are the phrase lengths in terms of measures?

    b. What is the cadence plan for this composition?

    c. Observe the editor's note regarding the rhythm ("meter") of this composition. What are the pros and cons of this suggestion?

Romance, from Faschingsschwank aus Wien, Op. 26, Robert Schumann

*The editor submits that the rhythm of this piece is in triple, not duple time, and that it should be understood in the following sense:

Academic conventions in Schumann's day would have frowned upon this kind of freedom, now in current use. The short measure in 2/8 time seems to respond perfectly to the nature of the theme, and the entire piece will be found to gain in unity when the same rhythmical pulse is observed throughout. The value of the quarter-notes remains, of course, unchanged in any case.

3. Discussion of Ross Lee Finney's *Fantasy in Two Movements, for Solo Violin* (excerpt, measures 1—57).

   a. What are the principal ways in which the composer achieves unity (of materials and structure) in this composition?

   b. Briefly discuss the rhythmic aspects of this excerpt. Where and how does the composer rhythmically prepare for the *Allegretto* ♩ = ca. 112 of the last measure?

   c. Is there a strong tonal orientation or "key feeling" in this excerpt from the *Fantasy*? Give specific reasons for your answer.

Excerpt from *Fantasy in Two Movements,* for Solo Violin, Ross Lee Finney

I. Statement and Variation

Chapters 1 – 12

REVIEW

1. Music is the _____ and _____ of organized sound.

2. Concerning the aesthetics of music, there are two principal views: that music is a heteronomous art capable of expressing_____ - _____ elements, and that music is an autonomous art and may realize only _____ principles and ideas.

3. The basic materials of music are _____ and _____ .

4. The science of acoustics is typically divided into four categories: _____ , _____ , _____ , and _____ .

5. _____ refers to the number of vibrations per second effected by an elastic body when the equilibrium of this body is in some way _____ .

6. Amplitude is the measurement of _____ .

7. A single note consists of a _____ and an additional complex called the _____ _____ .

8. The development of Western music corresponds in a general way to the_____ _____ .

9. Rhythm, melody, harmony, and color are the_____ of music.

10. Monophony, heterophony, polyphony, and homophony are specific kinds of _____ .

11. The invention of the staff is credited to_____ _____ _____ .

12. The basis for the notational system of the Middle Ages was the _____ .

13. The standard notation in use today is derived from _____ , a system established by _____ _____ _____ .

14. Notation provides for the _____ of the sound it represents.

15. Temperament refers to the _____ _____ for the subdivision of the octave.

16. _____ _____ divides the octave into twelve equal parts.

17. Discussion of the entire twelve modes is contained in a sixteenth-century publication by _____ , entitled _____ .

18. The range of the chant is termed the _____ .

19. The concluding tone of the chant is called the _____ .

20. The concept of the three hexachords,_____ , _____ , and _____ , is crucial to the understanding of music during the Medieval and Renaissance eras.

21. The decrease in distance by a semi-tone of a perfect interval results in _____ quality; the increase in distance by a semi-tone results in _____ quality.

22. There are two categories of minor scales, _____ and _____ , as determined by their _____ to the major tonic.

23. A _____ cadence has the tonic in both the bass and the soprano of the final chord.

24. The _____ cadence is the familiar "Amen" cadence.

25. Rhythm denotes the organization of _____ and _____.

26. The three general classifications of rhythm are _____, _____, and _____ rhythm.

27. _____ _____ is the most common temporal organization in Western music.

28. Metrical schemes are derived from _____ _____, introduced probably by _____ shortly before _____.

29. The terms *simple* and *compound meter* refer to the _____ of the _____.

30. A subdivision which relates to another meter is called a _____ _____.

31. The tonic accent refers to a _____ _____; an _____ accent results from a longer duration of a note.

32. *Hemiola,* when referring to time values, denotes the relationship of _____.

33. The term _____ is used to describe compositions that are notated in more than one meter simultaneously.

34. Dramatic shape of a melody refers to the _____ formed by the successive pitches.

35. Melody of all periods and by all composers shows an interchange between_____ and _____ motion.

36. Voice exchange between two parts without interval or octave modification is called _____.

37. In a composition using imitative devices, the leading voice is called _____, and the voice making the repetition is called the _____.

38. An entire composition in imitation is called _____.

39. The treatise *Gradus ad Parnassum* by _____ deals with the systematic study of _____ _____.

40. The fourth species consists of _____ notes of counterpoint for each note of *cantus firmus* and further includes the use of _____ notes and a device called _____.

41. Monophony and polyphony emphasize the _____ dimension of music; _____ underscores the vertical dimension; _____ is a combination of these two dimensions.

42. Alberti bass consists of _____ - _____ figurations.

43. Spatial organization is often thought of as a _____ dimension, especially in orchestral music.

44. _____ denotes the quality or "color" of a tone.

45. Transpositions are named according to the note that sounds when a written _____ is played.

46. Any instrument sounding a major second lower must be written a _____ _____ _____ than the desired concert pitch.

47. Standard instruments which transpose are the _____, _____, _____, and _____.

48. In instrumental combinations, the principle of vertical balance is achieved by agreement with the _____ _____ , _____ _____ , and _____ .

49. Horizontal balance in traditional scoring involves three different considerations: _____ _____ , _____ _____ , and _____ _____ .

50. _____ balance provides for both contrast and unity.

51. _____ is the combination of separate substances, elements, or subordinate parts into a new construction or composition.

52. Wallace Berry states that "form is the sum of those qualities in a piece of music that _____ _____ its parts and _____ the whole."

53. Investigation of Western music from all periods seems to suggest _____ _____ that apply in varying degrees to broad categories of musical design.

54. The principle of contrast of musical ideas is represented by the _____ and _____ forms, which are outlined as follows: _____ and _____ .

55. The principle of contrast of tonal schemes is demonstrated in the _____ or _____ _____ form, which is outlined _____ .

56. The principle of repetition is shown in the _____ , _____ , _____ _____ , and _____ _____ forms.

57. An important principle of musical organization is that of _____ , in which an idea is subjected to a changing environment or is constantly _____ .

58. A few of the variation forms of early music are _____ , _____ , _____ , and _____ .

59. Most canons follow the principle of _____ .

60. The principle of *contiguity* denotes a constantly evolving matrix of sound. A German term having similar implications is _____ .

Chapter 9
ARS ANTIQUA AND ARS NOVA

STUDIES

Briefly, but clearly, define the following terms and concepts.

1. The Tertian system

2. Ars Antiqua

3. Clausula

4. Motet

5. Rondel

6. Rondeau

7. Conductus

8. Successive counterpoint

9. Ars Nova

10. Hocket

11. Syncopation

12. Isorhythm

13. *Messe de Notre Dame*

14. Talea

15. "Machaut cadence" (see example 150)

Chapter 10
THE FIFTEENTH CENTURY: PRECURSORS OF MODERN MUSIC

STUDIES

Using the chart on page 142, Example 158, notate common cadences before 1600. Use the notes "d or d^i" as *finals*.

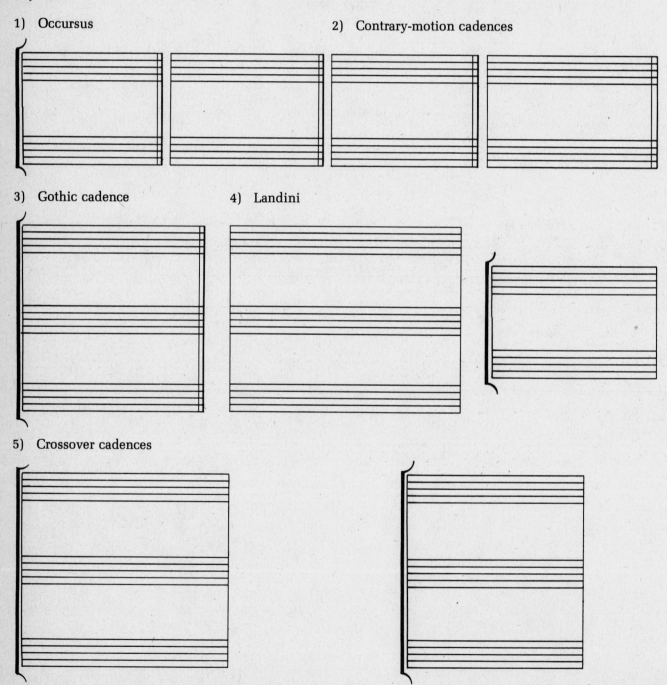

1) Occursus

2) Contrary-motion cadences

3) Gothic cadence

4) Landini

5) Crossover cadences

2. Compose a short piece of about 12 measures that illustrates either English discant or fauxbourdon. Use Examples 161 and 162 as models.

Chapter 11
MUSIC OF THE SIXTEENTH CENTURY

STUDIES

1. Transpose Example 177 of the text to the key of D major. Compose an additional eight measures using the same vocabulary, doublings, spacings, and general partwriting procedures observed in the example.

2. In four voices, correctly notate the following harmonic cadences in the keys indicated.

3.

a. Diagram the phrase structure of the entire *villancico* by Juan del Encina.

b. Circle the *root* of each chord in measures 1—11.

c. The cadence in measure 28 is _____ ; in measure 39 is _____.

d. The principal tonal center of the entire piece is _____.

Villancico, *Soy contento y vos servido*, Juan del Encina (1468—1529)

4. Write four-voice structures as indicated from the given soprano and bass notes. All triads *must* have two roots, one third, and one fifth.

a. Open structure

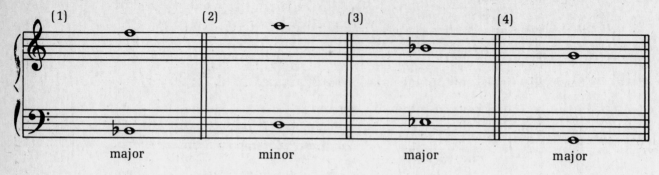

(1) major (2) minor (3) major (4) major

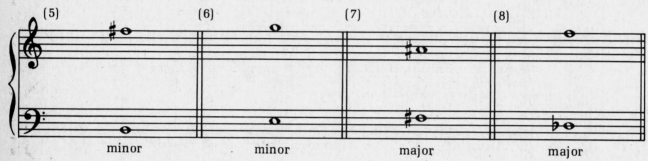

(5) minor (6) minor (7) major (8) major

b. Close structure

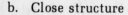
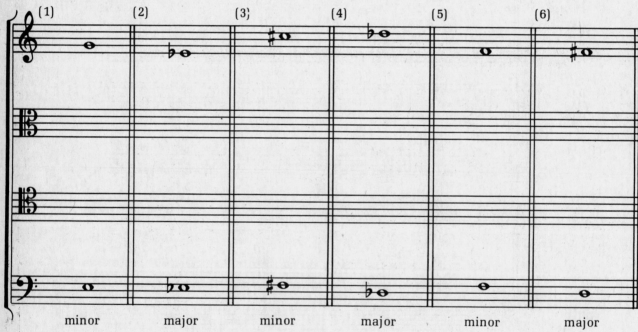

(1) minor (2) major (3) minor (4) major (5) minor (6) major

5. Mark all root movements as indicated on the next page. Circle all chords that do not contain two roots, one third, and one fifth.

78

Psalm Setting, *Mon Dieu me paist,*
from the French Psalter of 1565, Claude Goudimel (c. 1505—1572)

6. Part-writing in four voices.

Complete to four voices, using major and minor triads in root position.

a. Close structure

b. Close structure

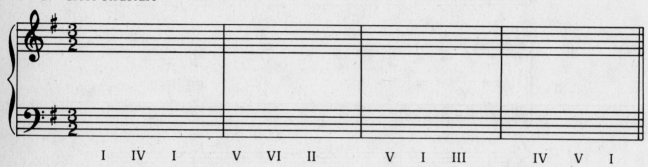

I   IV   I   V   VI   II   V   I   III   IV   V   I

c. Open structure

Chapter 12
BASIC PART WRITING IN FOUR VOICES

STUDIES

1. Change of structure.

   Change from open to close structure (or reverse) as indicated.

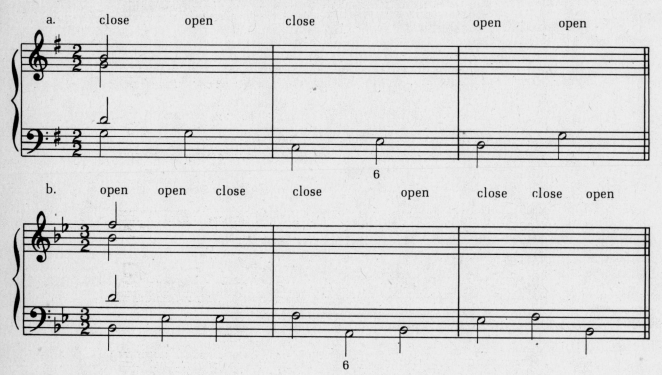

2. Suspension figures.

   a. Add suspensions as indicated.

b. Circle all suspensions in the Cristobal Morales *Magnificat*. Indicate 2—1, 4—3, (6—5), 7—6, or 9—18, as shown by example.

Magnificat Octavi Toni, Cristobal Morales
(ca. 1500—1553)

3. Analyze the following example in terms of:
   Root movement
   Melodic motion
   Structure of chords; changes in structure
   Doublings
   Non-harmonic tones: passing tones and suspensions
   Sixth chords

O Bone Jesu (complete), attributed to Giovanni Pierluigi da Palestrina (1524–1594)

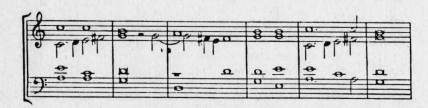

84

Measures 1–18, *Ave Verum Corpus*, William Byrd (1543–1623)

4. Analyze *Ave Verum Corpus* in the following terms:
    a. The rhythmic-melodic factors or organization

    b. The root movement of chords

    c. The relationship of each chord to the tonal axes G and B♭. (Mark with Roman numerals on the score)
    d. The identification of all non-chord tones (mark on score)
    e. The musical organization as a whole in terms of unification and diversity

5. Harmonic vocabulary and tonality.

Provide an harmonic and tonal analysis for John Dowland's lute air.

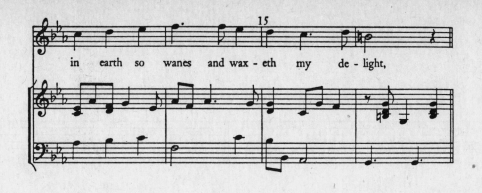

in earth so wanes and wax - eth my de - light,

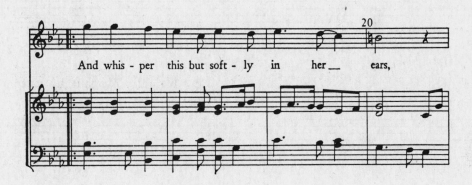

And whis - per this but soft - ly in her __ ears,

hope oft doth hang the head, and trust __ shed tears.

6. Non-chord tones.

Illustrate the following non-chord tones with four-part examples.

    a. Passing tones   b. Suspension

    c. Changing tones   d. Neighboring (auxiliary) tones

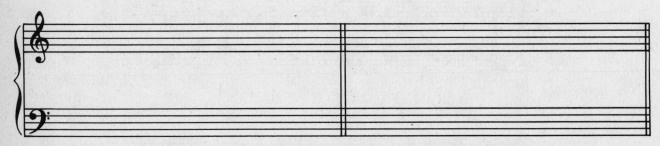

    e. Appoggiatura (a non-chord tone approached   f. Escape tone (échappée)
        by leap and realized by step—the dissonance
        occurs on the strong beat)

7. The six-four chord.

Notate six-four chords as indicated.

EXAMPLE: Passing $\frac{6}{4}$ in G Major

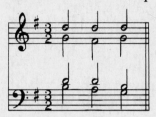

a. Cadential $\frac{6}{4}$ in b minor

b. Stationary $\frac{6}{4}$ in E♭ Major

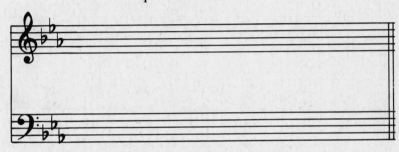

c. Arpeggiated $\frac{6}{4}$ in d minor

8. Invent inner voices for the given soprano and bass. Provide an harmonic analysis and identify all cadences.

Adapted from Guillaume Costeley (1531–1606)

9. Complete to four voices, except where rests are indicated. Include an harmonic analysis.

Adapted from Christopher Tye (c. 1500–c. 1572)

10. Complete the figured bass to four parts. Use close structure and regular doublings. Include an harmonic analysis.

NOTE: All chords marked 6 are chords of first inversion. All other sets of numbers 9 — 8, 7 — 6, 4 — 3, and 2 — 1 are *suspensions* above the bass note.

11. Invent two inner voices to the given soprano and bass.

From John Dowland (1562—1626)

12.

In G major (*allegro*, duple meter), invent a four-voice piece
from the given Roman numerals:

$$\begin{array}{ccccccccc} \text{I} & \text{IV}_6 & \text{V} & \text{I}_6 & \text{ii}_6 & \text{V} & \text{vi} & \text{IV} & \text{V} \\ \text{V/vi} & \text{vi} & \text{V}_6 & \text{I} & \text{IV} & \text{ii} & \text{V} & \text{I} \\ \text{IV}_6 & \text{V}_{43} & \text{I} & || \end{array}$$

13. Add three lower voices to the given soprano and numerals. (All notes marked + are to be treated as nonchord tones.)

From Michael Praetorius (1571–1621)

14. Compose a short original composition (about 14 measures) using the concepts and vocabulary that have been introduced in Chapter 12.

15. Compose an accompaniment (keyboard, lute, or guitar) for the following solo line. Use Example 207 as a model.

No. 53, *Aria da Stanza,* Cosimo Bottegari

From *The Bottegari Lutebook* (Wellesley Edition **No. 8, 1965),** ed. Carol MacClintock. Used by permission.

16. Analysis of *D'une Coline*.

D'une Coline. Claude le Jeune (1528-1600)

Dessus / Cinquiesme

D'u-ne co-li-ne m'y prou-me-nant Par la plu vert' et plu gay — e sai-zon

Taille

Quand tou-te cho - se rid au chams, Je voy u - ne Rô - ze ver - meil-lé - te

Qui tou-te fleu-ré-te de fleur de beau - té Pas - se de bien loin.

Rechant à 3

Je la voy de loin, Et je l'ai — me fort, Je la veu cueil-lir,

Et la main j'y tens, Mais las c'est en vain.

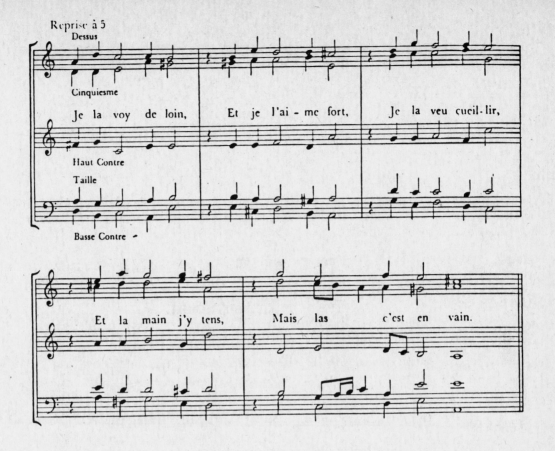

Prepare the analysis of *D'une Coline* in the following terms:

    a.   The meaning of *vers mesure*; the special metric-rhythmic features of this work

    b.   A comparison of three- and five-part texture to four-part writing

    c.   The design (form) of the composition

    d.   The extent and type of repetition

    e.   The shape of each line; the kinds of motion between the outside voices

    f.   The root movement (mark score)

    g.   Identification of non-chord tones (mark score)

    h.   The relationship of this analysis to performance

Chapter 13
SACRED POLYPHONY OF THE LATE SIXTEENTH CENTURY

STUDIES

1. Transpose *Oculus Non Vidit* down a perfect fifth. Copying works of master composers is one of the oldest and best ways to learn the craft of composition. Further, a performance version for male and female voices will have been effected.

Motet: OCULUS NON VIDIT from *Cantiones Duarum Vocum*   Lasso

STUDIES

2. Using *Oculus Non Vidit* as a model, compose about 12 measures employing modal counterpoint. Try for thirds, sixths, and tenths on strong beats; resolve all dissonances; avoid extensive disjunct motion; imitate Lasso's final cadence.

3. Summarize the principles of harmonic and polyphonic writing of the 16th century as suggested by the examples in chapters 12 and 13. Cite three or four points for each of the following: rhythm, melody, harmony, texture, and form.

Chapters 11 – 13

REVIEW

1. Circle the roots of the following triads:

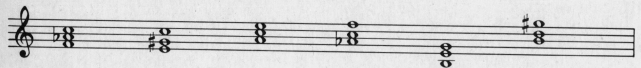

2. Describe the root movement of the following progressions (by seconds, thirds, etc.):

   a.

   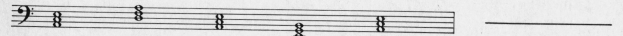

   b.

   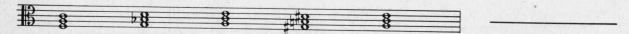

   c.

   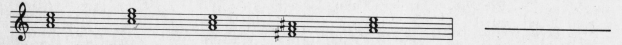

   d.

   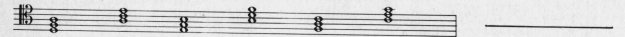

3. Doublings.

   a. The most common note doubled in a major or minor triad in root position is the _____.

   b. In the progression V—VI (especially in a minor key), it is best to double the _____.

4. Part-write the following progressions in the structures indicated.

   a. Close structure: I vi IV V iii IV I

   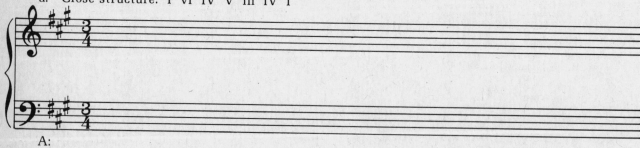

   A:

102

b. Open structure: i III iv V VI ii° V i

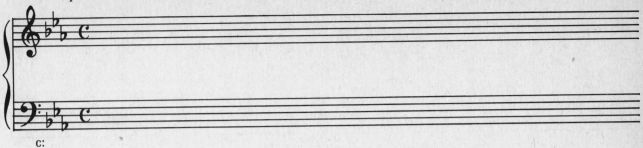

c:

5. Change of structure within the phrase may be accomplished in any of at least three different circumstances. These are:

a. _____

b. _____

c. _____

6. Non-chord tones and embellishing tones.

a. A suspension consists of three distinct parts. These are:

(1) _____

(2) _____

(3) _____

b. Illustrate the following suspensions (in four-voice part-writing). Be sure all three steps are present.

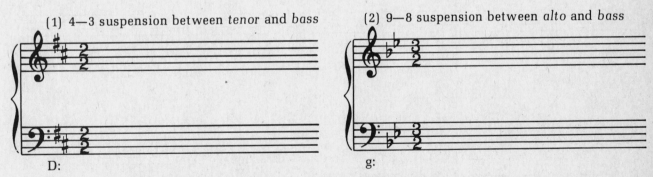

(1) 4—3 suspension between *tenor* and *bass*

D:

(2) 9—8 suspension between *alto* and *bass*

g:

c. Fill in the proper embellishing tones where indicated (+).

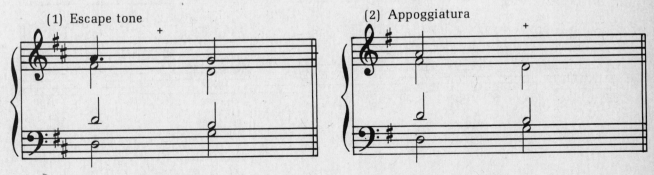

(1) Escape tone

(2) Appoggiatura

(3) Changing tones   (4) Cambiata

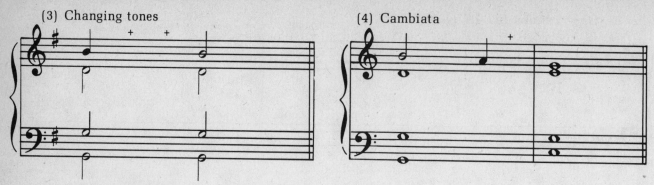

7. Irregular doublings.

    a. With a chord in first inversion (sixth chord), most often the _____ is doubled.

    b. With a diminished triad, it is best to double the _____ .

    c. With a chord in second inversion (six-four chord), most often the _____ is doubled.

    d. With an augmented triad, it is best to double the _____ .

8. Secondary function.

    Illustrate the following secondary dominants with their resolutions.

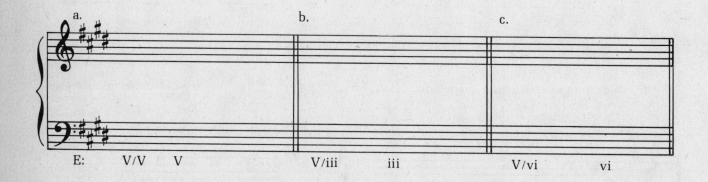

E: V/V   V   V/iii   iii   V/vi   vi

9. Six-four chords.

    Illustrate the following six-four chords.

    a. Cadential six-four   b. Passing six-four

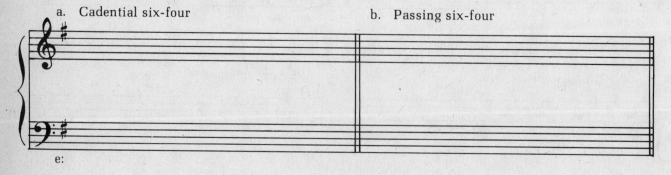

e:

10. Late sixteenth-century polyphony.
    Discuss the Victoria and van Werth examples in the following terms.

    a. Root movement.

    b. Use of inversions.

    c. Use of passing tones and suspensions.

    d. Melodic and harmonic rhythm.

    e. Triad doublings (van Werth only).

Excerpt from *o vos omnes*, Tomas Luis de Victoria (c. 1540—1611)

Madrigal, *Cara la vita*, Jacob van Werth (1536—1596)

From Archibald T. Davison and Willi Apel, *Historical Anthology of Music*. Copyright 1946, 1949 by the President and Fellows of Harvard College. Used by permission of the Harvard Universtiy Press.

Chapter 14
THEORETICAL CONCEPTS AND
PRACTICES OF THE BAROQUE ERA
(c. 1600–1750)

STUDIES

1. Definitions.
   Define the following terms briefly and clearly.

   a. Functional harmony:

   b. Altered chords:

   c. Modulation:

   d. Bi-modality (interchangeability of modes):

   e. Secondary function:

2. Complete to five parts (close structure). Comment briefly on each of the following items:
    The phrase structure
    The types of cadences
    The implied tonal orientation (level) at each cadence
    The kinds of root movement

Exultent Caeli, Claudio Monteverdi

*Sharp added to signature, note values halved.

3. Continue the realization of the given figured bass with three or four voices.

Solo recitative from *Orfeo*, Claudio Monteverdi

Excerpt from *Orfeo*, Claudio Monteverdi

4. The questions refer to the excerpt from *Orfeo* by Monteverdi.

    a. The kinds of root movement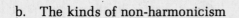

    b. The kinds of non-harmonicism

    c. The extent and kind of repetition

    d. The kinds of compositional devices

PROGRAM XI

Modulation

1. MODULATION

    1. One means of achieving tonal and harmonic variety within a piece of music is to move from one tonal center to another. This is known as *modulation*. When the tonal emphasis is shifted away from a preexistent key to a new key, a _____ has occurred.

2. KEY (or TONALITY)

    2. Although a new key signature need not be applied in all cases, a modulation is, in effect, a change of _____.

3. PERMANENT

    3. Depending on its length and importance, a modulation may be termed either *transient* or *permanent*. If the new key is emphasized only slightly or is passed over quickly, the modulation is transient. However, if the new tonic is firmly established after the modulation, the modulation is _____.

4. TRANSIENT

    4. If a new tonic key is merely suggested or appears briefly, the modulation is said to be _____ .

5. COMMON-CHORD

    5. Modulations are also classified according to the process used to relate one tonal area to another. The classification includes *diatonic*, *chromatic*, and *enharmonic* modulations. Diatonic modulations are also called *common-chord* modulations. If the same chord appears unaltered in two keys, it is a _____-_____ modulation.

6. A MINOR (A,C,E)

    6. A chart of the triads that appear diatonically in the key of C major is given on the first staff of the following example. Below it are charts that show how the triads of two closely related keys, F major and G major, coincide with those of C major.

    C major, principal tonic

    F major, closely related on the flat side

    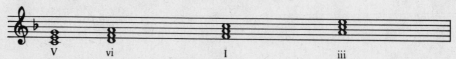

    G major, closely related on the sharp side

    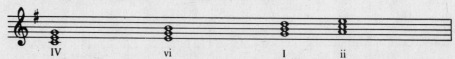

    For a triad to be considered a common chord, it must be found unaltered by accidentals in at least two keys. For example, notice the C major triad—C,E,G. This chord not only serves as tonic in C major, but as dominant in F major and subdominant in G major. It appears in all three keys without chromatic alterations and is therefore known as a common chord.

    Which other triad, besides that in C major, appears diatonically in all three keys—C major, F major, and G major? _____ .

7. NO; BECAUSE THE G MAJOR TRIAD DOES NOT APPEAR DIATONICALLY IN F MAJOR	7. Since an A minor triad appears in all three tonalities above, it could be used to effect a common-chord modulation from C major to either F major or G major. Could a G major triad be used to negotiate a common-chord modulation to F major? Why or why not? _____ _____.
8. I I V I IV	8. Below is an example of a diatonic, or common-chord, modulation. Study and play the example at the piano. Then supply a Roman numeral analysis for all triads up to and including the chord marked with an asterisk. (The proper figured bass is given.)

Uns ist ein Kindlein heut' gebor'n, J. S. Bach

9. C MAJOR; PERFECT AUTHENTIC	9. The phrase in the example in frame 8 begins in G major. However, the final cadence is in a new tonality. Name this new key and the type of cadence (i.e., authentic, plagal, deceptive, perfect, imperfect, etc.): _____ ; _____.
10. NO	10. In the excerpt in frame 8, is the chord immediately following the one with the asterisk a diatonic chord in G major? (yes/no)
11. I	11. In frame 8, the chord with the asterisk is a IV chord in G major. What is the Roman numeral analysis of this chord in C major? _____.
12. COMMON CHORD	12. Since the chord with the asterisk (C,E,G) appears diatonically in both G major and C major, it can effect a common-chord modulation. The chord following this (F,A,C) is diatonic in only one of the keys (C major) and cannot be considered a _____ _____. (Therefore, the modulation has already occurred prior to the appearance of the F major triad.)
13. I IV V I	13. Complete the Roman numeral analysis of this phrase in the key of C major.

Uns ist ein Kindlein heut' gebor'n, J.S. Bach

14. No Response

14. In the excerpt in frame 13 notice the technique of Roman numeral analysis. The Roman numerals that designate the harmonic function of the common-chord in both keys are bracketed. A pitch letter next to the bracket shows the new tonality, while the harmonic analysis is continued at a different level. This is an immediate visual aid to show that a modulation has occurred.

15. No Response

15. There is a subcategory of common-chord modulations known as *bi-modality*, or interchangeability of modes. When there is no change of key center, yet chords appear from the parallel minor (or major) of the existing key, a change of mode is in effect. Since there is no change of key center involved, this technique cannot be termed a true modulation.

16. A^b MINOR;
A^b MAJOR

16. The fragment below is by Schubert. Study and play it at the piano. What is the tonality at the beginning of the excerpt? _____. At the end? ___

Impromptu, Op. 90, No. 4, Franz Schubert

17. Bi-MODALITY, or INTERCHANGE-ABILITY OF MODES

17. The tonality of the Schubert example is firmly established as A^b, yet it fluctuates between a^b minor and A^b major. This "harmonic borrowing" between the parallel major and minor keys is called _____-_____, or _____ ___ _____.

18. $\underline{a^b}$: $\underline{i}$ $\underline{iv}$ $\underline{i}_6^4$

$\underline{iv}_6$ $\underline{i}_6^4$ $\underline{V}$

$\underline{A^b}$: $\underline{I}$

18. Supply a Roman numeral analysis for the example given in frame 16. (Be careful to distinguish between major and minor triads by using upper-case Roman numerals for the former and lower-case ones for the latter.)

___: _____ _____ _____ _____ _____ _____ _____: _____

STUDIES

1. In four parts, write the *dominant of the dominant* (V/V) in the keys indicated.

EXAMPLE:

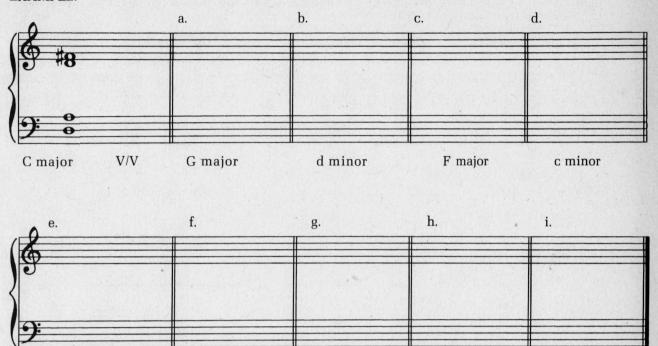

C major   V/V   G major   d minor   F major   c minor

A major   E♭ major   B♭ major   b minor   e minor

2. Illustrate the following examples of *secondary function*.

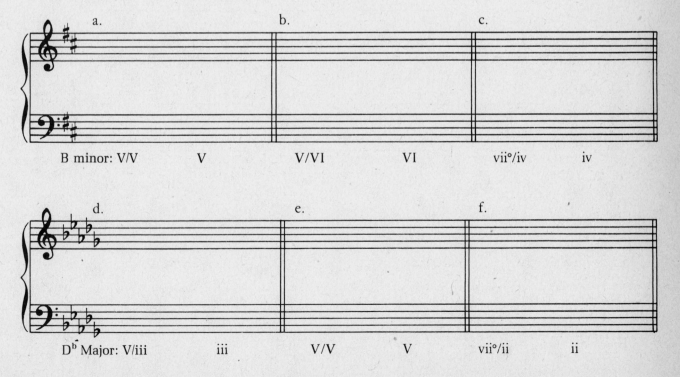

B minor: V/V   V   V/VI   VI   vii°/iv   iv

D♭ Major: V/iii   iii   V/V   V   vii°/ii   ii

3. Modulation.

   The following items refer to Domenico Scarlatti's *Sonata in B Minor*, Longo 33. There are numerous "suggested" or transient modulations within this sonata. Identify at least twelve of these in the manner shown.

Measure(s)	Suggested Key Area	How Effected
		$b: i = f\# \ iv \ (V_{\substack{6 \\ 4 \\ 3}} \ i)$

EXAMPLE:

| 5–6 | f# minor | |

a. _____   _____   _____

b. _____   _____   _____

c. _____   _____   _____

d. _____   _____   _____

e. _____   _____   _____

f. _____   _____   _____

g. _____   _____   _____

h. _____   _____   _____

i. _____   _____   _____

j. _____   _____   _____

k. _____   _____   _____

l. _____   _____   _____

Sonata in B Minor, Longo 33, Domenico Scarlatti

Andante mosso

118

PROGRAM XII

SEVENTH CHORDS

1. ADDING A THIRD
    TO ANY TRIAD

1. An additional third may be added to any triad, forming a seventh with the root, and effecting a chord of the seventh.

Chords of the seventh are formed by _____ .

2. TRIAD QUALITY,
    DISTANCE FROM
    THE CHORD ROOT
    TO THE
    SEVENTH

2. Seventh chords of different *color* or quality are derived from the major and harmonic minor scales. Although terminology varies, a logical nomenclature identifies first the triad quality (major, minor, diminished, augmented), and second the distance from the chord root to the seventh (major, minor, diminished, augmented). The names of seventh chords are determined by _____ and _____ .

3. mm dm Mm MM dd

3. These seventh chords have various qualities.

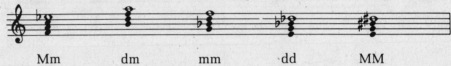

What are the qualities of the following seventh chords?

____   ____   ____   ____   ____   ____

4. MM mm mm MM
    Mm mm dm

4. The seventh chords that result from the major scale are frequently used. What are their qualities?

____   ____   ____   ____   ____   ____   ____

5. mM dm AM mm
    Mm MM dd

5. What are the qualities of the seventh chords resulting from the harmonic minor scale?

____   ____   ____   ____   ____   ____   ____

6. dM, AA, Ad

6. What are the qualities of these unusual seventh chords?

_____   _____   _____

7.

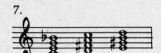

7. The triad with seventh, built on the fifth degree, common to both major and minor modes, was most frequently used in the seventeenth and eighteenth centuries. It is called *the dominant seventh* chord. Since the addition of the seventh does not alter the triad function, seventh chords are frequently employed as secondary function.

EXAMPLE:

C: V⁷/ii   V⁷/iii

In C major, show the following chords:

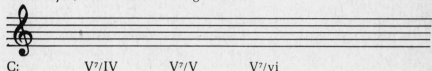

C: V⁷/IV   V⁷/V   V⁷/vi

8. 7 or 7
   5
   3

8. Seventh chords occur in root position and three inversions. When the root of the seventh chord is in the bass, its figured bass notation is $\frac{7}{5}$ or 7. EXAMPLE:

$$\frac{7}{5} \text{ or } 7$$

The figured bass notation for a seventh chord whose root is in the bass is _____ or _____ .

9. 6 or 6
   5   5
   3

9. When the third of a seventh chord occurs in the bass, its figured bass notation is $\frac{6}{5}$ or $\frac{6}{5}$. EXAMPLE:

$$\frac{6}{5} \text{ or } \frac{6}{5}$$

The figured bass notation for a seventh chord whose third is in the bass is _____ or _____ .

10. 6 or 4
    4   3
    3

10. When the fifth of a seventh chord occurs in the bass, its figured bass notation is $\frac{6}{4}$ or $\frac{4}{3}$. EXAMPLE:

$$\frac{6}{4} \text{ or } \frac{4}{3}$$

The figured bass notation for a seventh chord whose fifth is in the bass is _____ or _____ .

11. 6 or 4 or 2
    4   2
    2

11. When the seventh of a seventh chord occurs in the bass, its figured bass notation is $\frac{6}{4}$ or $\frac{4}{2}$ or 2. EXAMPLE:

$$\frac{6}{4} \text{ or } \frac{4}{2} \text{ or } 2$$

The figured bass notation for a seventh chord whose seventh is in the bass is _____ or _____ or _____ .

12. a. 7 b. (6) c. ♭7
    (5)   4   (5)
    (3) ♭3   (3)

   d. (6)   e. 6
      4   ♭5
      2   (3)

12. Accidentals appearing above the bass or lowest note must be shown in the figured bass. Indicate the figured bass for the following seventh chords:

EXAMPLES: a.   b.   c.   d.   e.

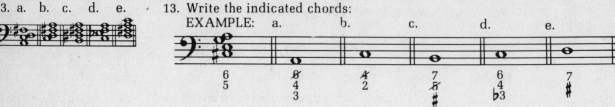

13. a. b. c. d. e.

13. Write the indicated chords:
EXAMPLE: a.   b.   c.   d.   e.

14. STEP-WISE
    DOWN

14. Since the initial use of sevenths resulted from linearity, it is reasonable to observe that the *preparation* and *resolution* of chordal sevenths are based on melodic considerations. The usual resolution of any minor seventh is step-wise down. Minor sevenths of a chord usually resolve _____ .

15. NO RESPONSE

15. The preparation of the chordal seventh is as a passing-tone figure, a suspension figure, an upper-auxiliary figure, or as an appoggiatura figure.

16. a. SUSPENSION
      FIGURE
   b. APPOGGIATURA
      FIGURE
   c. PASSING-TONE
      FIGURE
   d. UPPER-
      AUXILIARY
      FIGURE

16. Identify the preparation figures of the seventh in the following chords.

a. _____   b. _____

c. _____   d. _____

STUDIES

Seventh Chords.

a.   Notate seventh chords as indicated.

EXAMPLES:

R—Mm   3rd—Mm   7—dd

(1)   (2)   (3)

R—Mm   R—mm   3rd—mM

(4)   (5)   (6)

3rd—Mm   7—mm   5th—AM

(7)   (8)   (9)   (10)

7th—MM   5th—dd   3rd—dm   R—MM

b.   Resolve the following *dominant*-sevenths to the implied tonics (tonic may be either major or minor).

EXAMPLE:

Chapter 15
THE MAJOR-MINOR SYSTEM OF TONAL MUSIC

STUDIES

1. Cadences
   Using the example below, write ii$^6_5$ V cadences in the indicated keys. Label the chords.

Example.

E minor

i   ii$^6_5$ V$^{87}_\sharp$ i

a.

G minor

b.

D minor

c.

C minor

d.

D major

2. Cadences
   Transpose the following to the keys indicated.

Example:

G minor

i   VI   vii°7/V V8 7
                          4 3

a.

E minor

b.

A minor

c.

D minor

d.

F major

3. Augmented Sixth Chords.

  a. Do an harmonic analysis of each of the following musical examples containing augmented sixth chords.

(1) From *Io pur respiro* (c. 1600), Gesualdo (in *HAM*, Vol. I, p. 182)

(NOTE: The g#[i], in measure 1 and the d#[i] in measure 4 were ab[i] and eb[i] in the original.)

(2) Chorale, *Ich Hab' Mein' Sach Gott Heimgestellt*, J.S. Bach

(3) *Piano Sonata*, K. 283. Second Movement, W. A. Mozart

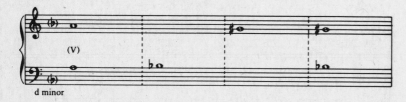

  b. Writing Augmented Sixth Chords.

  The two notes of the augmented sixth interval can be found by first locating the *dominant*, then writing the bass note a semi-tone higher (with a different letter name) and the upper voice a semi-tone lower (with a different letter name).

Augmented Sixth Interval

To the augmented sixth interval should be added the *tonic note* (in this case d[i]), and then whichever note is needed to give it the color of the three different kinds of augmented sixth chords:

  (1) Add another tonic for an Italian sixth ($^6_3$).

  (2) Add a fifth from the bass for a German sixth ($^6_5$).

  (3) Add a tritone from the bass for a French sixth ($^6_4{}_3$).

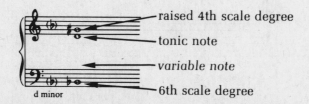

raised 4th scale degree

tonic note

variable note

6th scale degree

4. Write the following augmented sixth chords (with their correct resolutions).

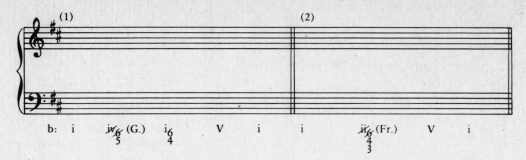

b: i   iv$^6_5$(G.)   i$^6_4$ V   i   i   ii^6(Fr.)   V   i
                                                      $^4_3$

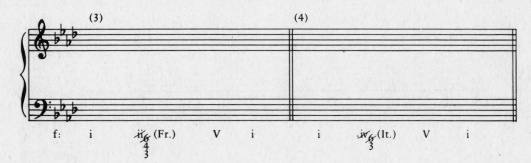

f: i   ii^6(Fr.)   V   i   i   iv^6(It.)   V   i
          $^4_3$ ^{3}

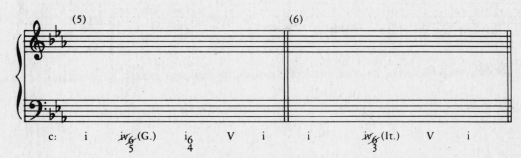

c: i   iv$^6_5$(G.)   i$^6_4$ V   i   i   iv^6(It.)   V   i
                                                      ^{3}

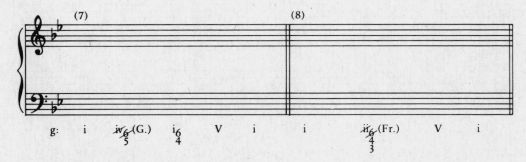

g: i   iv$^6_5$(G.)   i$^6_4$ V   i   i   ii^6(Fr.)   V   i
                                                      $^4_3$

5. Part-Writing the Neapolitan Sixth Chord.

   a. Review pp. 227–228 of text.
   b. In four voices, write examples of the Neapolitan sixth chord in the indicated keys.

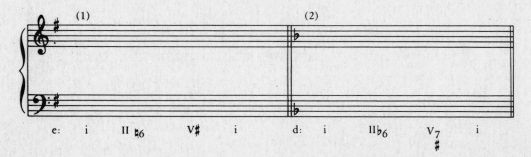

e: i   II♮6   V♯   i   d: i   II♭6   V$_7$ i
                                                  ♯

6. In four parts, realize the following figured bass lines. Identify and label all augmented sixth and Neapolitan sixth chords. Provide an harmonic analysis.

a. Grave

b. Andante

7. Invent a complementary period to the aria with figured bass given in Example 000. Realize the figured bass in manner and style appropriate for performance as an accompaniment.

Purcell

8. Analysis of Baroque Suite (Handel Suite XV, complete). Respond to the following items of discussion.

    a. Meter, tempo, and general form of each movement.

      Allemande:

      Courante:

      Sarabande:

      Gigue:

    b. Relationship of materials (thematic ideas, harmonic progressions, etc.) between the Allemande and the Courante. What is the historical precedent for this relationship?

c.   Principal cadence plan for each movement.

Allemande:

Courante:

Sarabande:

Gigue:

d.   Briefly discuss the binary-ternary aspects of these movements.

Suite XV, George Frederick Handel

Allemande.

a) ... b) ... oder: ... c) Vgl. unter b) d) ... e) Vgl. unter b)

Peters Edition No. 4B. Reprinted by permission of G. F. Peters Corporation, 373 Park Avenue South, New York, N.Y. 10016.

Allegretto

Courante.

a)   b)   c) Vgl. unter a)

9. Keyboard realization of figured bass.
   Provide an appropriate realization for keyboard for Corelli's *Adagio* from the *Sonata da chiesa*, Opus 3, No. 7.

CORELLI, Sonata, Op. 3, No. 7

137